PAGE 32

PAGE 42

PAGE 76

FICTION

Contents

DC THOMSON MEDIA

Favourite Things

Shoes, kids and long baths – the *Strictly* girls tell all

Claudia Winkleman

Refreshingly down to earth, frank and funny, Claudia endears herself to us with her casual approach to life – and the way she puts her children and family first. Behind that deep fringe is a warm and spontaneous heart, which despite being a stellar star and one of the Beeb's highest paid personalities, still starts to flutter when she meets a fellow star unexpectedly – such as Christopher Biggins when out shopping in the supermarket! "I was so excited and just wanted to ask for his autograph," she says.

Gorgeous yet ever so slightly untidy, Claudia predictably shuns a polished look. "I don't like anything too perfect, or anyone who looks like they have just stepped out of a salon. Add a fringe and you can look messy and ramshackle but with a bit of oomph!

"My favourite things are walking through Hyde Park with my children and long soaks in my enormous bath." She loves cuddling up to watch films of an evening. 'I'd like my children to remember all the cuddles and bedtimes, and that I worshipped them unconditionally.' And her favourite films? *The Godfather* trilogy and *ET!*

Tess Daly

"Claudia and I have been friends for years. We talk about fashion all the time and what we're wearing on *Strictly Come Dancing*. We're in and out of each other's dressing rooms, scanning each other's clothes' rails: 'Oh! Jammy!'

"Clothes, shoes and children are our favourite subjects."

Tall and elegant, Tess always looks great in block colours or sharp monochrome styling. The mum-of-two admits great underwear is key when it comes to showcasing the sleek column dresses she loves. "Spanx are my best friend. They streamline your silhouette so clothes hang better and also hold your tummy in. Television is unforgiving so every little helps!"   **Continued overleaf**

More favourites overleaf and throughout the annual

Sparkly Style

The best accessory of all is a dazzling smile...

Holly And Fearne Friends Come First

"We're friends first and foremost," says Fearne of Holly, of a friendship which first began when they both worked in children's television at the BBC. The glamorous twosome have partied, holidayed together, completed charity work and have co-authored a book entitled *The Best Friends' Guide to Life.*

"You just find that you fit together. Your interests may be different but the same things make you laugh and cry," says Holly.

Sing Your Heart Out Shirley And Chums

Paul Simon

The muddy Glastonbury music festival seems like an unlikely setting for Dame Shirley Bassey but she is just one of many celebrity singers who have performed in the Living Legend slot, one of the highlights of the annual event. Dame Shirley jetted in from her home in Monte Carlo to take her place in the Glastonbury roll call, which over the years has also seen such illustrious names

Dolly Parton

as Paul Simon, Dolly Parton and even good old Sir Bruce Forsyth taking to the stage. Then a sprightly 71, Dame Shirley belted out a 40-minute set dressed in a typically glamorous frock – accessorised with a pair of custom-designed, diamond-monogrammed "DSB" Wellington boots, rumoured to have cost around £3,000!

Bruce Forsyth

Continued overleaf

Sport Of Queens

Follow the example of our active stars and get involved with sport, whether taking part or turning out to cheer others on!

Fern Britton

Our kind-hearted celebrities often lend their support to good causes. Keen cyclist Fern Britton has helped to raise millions of pounds for the Genesis Research Trust, completing endurance rides with teams of fundraisers in locations around the world.

Countess of Wessex

Last year the Countess was one of a team who raised £18,000 by cycling 445 miles from the Palace of Holyroodhouse in Edinburgh to Buckingham Palace in London, all in recognition of the 60th anniversary of the Duke of Edinburgh Award Scheme.

A Wow at Wimbledon

Between her royal duties and being a mum, there can't be much diary space for Kate to indulge in her favourite sports, which include hockey, tennis and skiing. But there are compensations for the ultra-sporty duchess, such as the best seats in the house at key events such as Wimbledon!

Lorraine Kelly, Footie Fan

Outdoor activities are more enjoyable without the need for waterproofs and thermals. Yet Lorraine Kelly routinely braves the elements to support her beloved Dundee United Football Club and whatever the weather, she always brings a ray of sunshine as she attends wearing her team's bright colours!

Flying High – Carol Vorderman

Brainy Carol Vorderman is used to passing her exams and she's been chalking up more qualifications since training for and completing her pilot's licence in 2014. While her mother's ill-health recently caused Carol to delay her plans to fly solo around the globe in Mildred, the twin-engine propeller plane she named after British aviator Mildred Bruce, she will still be clocking up the hours in her pilot's logbook when she can. Carol says, "It's going to be a great adventure."

Elaine Everest

Yesterday Once More

A clean break from her husband meant walking away from dog shows and all she loved… until now

ILLUSTRATIONS: GETTY IMAGES, ISTOCKPHOTO

J ennie gazed out of the coach window as dawn broke over the motorway. She'd made this journey so many times in the past… but this time it would be different.

She could recall every twist and turn in the roads from her home in Kent to the National Exhibition Centre in Birmingham along with all the essential stops to exercise the dogs and stretch her legs.

Back then she'd had Simon by her side to share the driving and prepare the dogs. Today, visiting Crufts as a spectator, was the first time in ten years that she'd ventured anywhere near a dog show since Simon had walked out of her life and moved in with her best friend, Gemma, a fellow exhibitor.

The reason Simon had left her was now snoozing beside her on the uncomfortable coach seat; their nine-year-old son, Josh, who looked like a mini-version of his father. If she missed one thing from her past life it was the dogs.

Jennie had arrived on her father's doorstep deep in shock, walking away from everything she'd held dear. Simon's confession and his words of accusation when, champagne chilling and a meal for two in the oven she'd announced that they were to be parents and he'd told her he was leaving.

Through the months that followed, her father encouraged her to plan for the future as a single mother, assuring her he'd be there every step of the way. She found a part-time office job dedicating herself to a future without Simon, who had accused Jennie of cramping his style.

In her heart of hearts she'd known he didn't desire the conservative family life she craved; he wanted nothing more than to travel the world exhibiting and judging dogs. Jennie had loved her past life breeding fit, healthy puppies and attending dog shows, but knew she'd never be free of Simon, seeing him with his new love at every turn if she were to continue. With an aching heart she'd turned her back on her old life, signing ownership of her dogs over to Simon and creating a future with her son.

I t was as Josh approached his ninth birthday he began to ask for a dog to join their little family.

"What do you think, Dad?" Jennie asked after she'd tucked Josh up in his bed for the night.

Continued overleaf

"I'll say the same as I told you when you were Josh's age. *If you have a puppy it is your sole responsibility and your mother and I will not help you*," he said with a small smile, remembering how seriously Jennie had taken her responsibilities.

It was Buster, a lovable sheepdog, who had led to Jennie wanting to join the world of dog showing and setting up her own grooming parlour, and how she had met Simon and made an ill-fated marriage.

Now she nodded in agreement.

"I'd hate to deny Josh the joy of growing up with a dog. Perhaps it is time he learned how to care for his own pet."

When the subject came up in

computer and a picture of you and Gramps with two dogs came up. It is you, isn't it? You do look funny with your hair like that," he chuckled.

Jennie stared at the image of her sitting with her dad and beside them, the first dogs she'd owned. The local newspaper had interviewed her when she'd attended her very first Crufts. It had been an exciting time when she'd qualified to attend the prestigious dog show.

"That was a long time ago. Gramps looks so young." She smiled as she gently touched the screen.

"That's the dog for me, please," he said looking at her with deep blue eyes that reminded her so much of Simon.

Her heart lurched. Would she ever

"I'd like a Border collie," Josh said excitedly. Jennie felt faint with shock

conversation the next day Jennie sat her son at the family computer and showed him the Kennel Club website. He spent many hours reading about puppies and the purpose of each different breed.

"I've chosen the dog I'd like to own," he announced excitedly one day when Jennie arrived home from work.

"I'll leave you too it," her father smiled heading to the kitchen.

Josh sat at the computer pointing to the screen. "I'd like a Border collie," he announced in excitement.

Jennie felt faint with the shock of seeing the breed she'd loved so much displayed on the computer screen.

"What made you decide this?" she asked trying to keep her question casual.

Josh grinned. "I put our name into the

forget her ex? Part of her loved him deeply and they'd shared a good life until… until Simon's indiscretion.

"Mum?" Josh nudged her. "Look, it says here that it's Crufts next month. Can we go and look at the dogs… please?"

Jennie knew once Josh had set his heart on something, there'd be no letting up.

"I'm not sure, Josh. It's a long journey."

"We can go by coach if you don't want to drive. Here, look at this."

With a click of the mouse, a list of coach companies appeared. Each one had trips arranged to take dog lovers from all corners of the UK to Birmingham and Crufts.

Jennie hesitated but knew that she, too, would like to visit Crufts and feel the excitement she missed so much.

"Mum?" her son prompted.

"Sorry, Josh. I was miles away. Yes, let's go and see the greatest dog show in the world."

Josh went off quite happily to have his bath while Jennie sat in the seat vacated by her excited son and booked the tickets. She'd lost contact with the people she'd known from her dog showing days and had purposely avoided reading the canine publications or looking online at show news. The memories had hurt too much.

"There's a small dog show on at Maidstone at the weekend," her father said, bringing in a cup of tea for them both. "Why not take Josh along and let him see the breeds in action? Border collies are scheduled. It would do you good to look up some old friends."

Jennie frowned.

"I don't know, Dad. What if…?"

"Simon won't be there. He has bigger fish to fry these days. The last I read, he was living in the States and doing the circuit over there."

"Dad?" She stared at him.

"Just because you don't keep in touch with the dog world doesn't mean I don't." He smiled. "I quite enjoyed helping you before you got yourself tied up with Slippery Simon."

Jennie grinned at her father's old name for her ex.

"Thanks, Dad. I can always rely on you," she said giving him an affectionate kiss on the cheek.

Continued overleaf

"Is this Crufts?" Josh asked as he gazed around the large agricultural hall in amazement. Everywhere people where either standing ready to go into the roped off rings to compete or were busy chatting to friends while grooming their dogs.

For Jennie it was like stepping back in time. Memories came rushing back of early-morning starts and the odour of dogs mixed with frying bacon from the little café at the side of the hall that was doing a roaring trade selling hot food and coffee in polystyrene cups.

"No, love, this is what is called an Open Show. Crufts has many more dogs than this. Now, where are the Border collies?"

'This way," her dad said, leading them changed at all. Where's the boy? I can't wait to meet him."

Jennie's questioning eyes met her dad's smiling gaze.

"I rang Connie as soon as I knew we were coming to the show. I thought she might help us with you-know-what?"

"I thought you might, Dad." Jennie grinned as she was hugged by the older woman and received a large wet lick from the puppy. "It's good to see you and be back with friends. I never expected this, to be honest. Josh, come and meet Connie and her puppy. Gramps bought me my first puppy from Connie," she explained.

Josh's eyes widened as he heard this and he was soon helping Connie as she explained how old the puppy was and what she had to do when he was taken

Memories rushed back of the odour of dogs mixed with frying bacon in the café

through a group of Labrador Retrievers that Josh wanted to stop and stroke.

"Don't touch the dogs, Josh, unless the owners give you permission," he called behind him to his grandson.

They stopped by a roped off area where Jennie could see a few familiar faces standing with Border collies of varying sizes and ages.

"Well I'll be blessed, look who it isn't," her father said, heading over to an elderly woman who was brushing a puppy on a grooming table. "If it isn't Connie Trentham as I live and breathe."

The elderly woman turned and hugged Jennie and her father. "Why, it's good to see you both. I was that pleased when you rang, Alan. The pair of you have hardly into the show ring, while her father went off the buy them all hot drinks. It may have been sunny outside but the hall still had a chill from the concrete floors and open doors that led to outside show rings.

"Jennie? It's never Jennie Carmichael?" a familiar voice said.

Turning, Jennie came face-to-face with a tall, dark-haired man with twinkling green eyes.

"Stuart? Gosh, I never expected to see you here. How are you?" she asked, stumbling over her words a little.

She felt her cheeks redden as she smiled up into his kind face.

"I have a boarding kennels down near the coast. Sophie's not been out much recently so we thought it would be good practice before Crufts. Come and meet her."

Jennie felt her heart plummet. She'd always had a soft spot for Stuart. He had a gentle side, which always got the best out of his dogs, and was strong and dependable when need be.

She recalled how he'd stepped in one year at Crufts when animal activists had got into the show and were bent on causing trouble. Yes, he was a man a woman could depend on. But who was Sophie?

She followed him towards the side of the hall where a large cage on wheels was parked, his kennel name engraved along one side. "Sophie, come and meet an old friend," he said, releasing a full-grown collie with a long, flowing coat.

Jennie breathed a sigh of relief, which surprised her. She'd not thought of another man in ten years after being treated so badly by her ex-husband.

"Hello, sweetie," she said, kneeling down and wrapping her arms around the dog. She breathed in the aroma of the warm clean coat. Memories come flooding back which brought tears to her eyes. She'd been a fool to keep away from thee world she loved so much.

"Oh how I've missed you all," she said.

"We've missed you too," Stuart replied.

Wake up, Josh, or you'll miss something amazing," Jennie said excitedly as she gently shook her son's shoulder.

Josh rubbed his eyes and stared out of the coach window. "I can only see rows

and rows of cars," he said grumpily.

"Yes, but what's *in* the cars?" Jennie prompted him.

This time Josh looked more carefully.

"Dogs – every car is full of dogs," he exclaimed. "I can't wait to get to Crufts!"

Inside the vast exhibition centre they followed a map from hall to hall until they came to a show ring where people mingled, waiting for the judging of Border collies to begin.

"So many dogs!" Josh grinned at Jennie as he flicked through a catalogue that listed all the dogs entered that day. "It's a shame Gramps couldn't come with us," he said as he opened the book on the pages containing entry after entry of their favourite breed. "There are hundreds of them. Cool!"

"Someone had to stay at home to care for Freddie. When he's old enough, we can go to dog shows together," she said, thinking of the small bundle of fun back home in Kent. It was meant to be, meeting Connie once more – and her having a litter of puppies just ready to go to the right homes.

Glancing across the green-carpeted show ring she spotted Stuart dressed in a smart three-piece suit holding Sophie's lead. He spotted the pair and raised his hand in greeting.

"Yes – it's all meant to be," she murmured to herself.

Turn over to find out more about best-selling author Elaine Everest.

A Moment With Elaine

The popular author tells us...

What inspires you to write?
As a teenager I devoured Nan's women's magazines and always read the short stories first. Even then my dream was to be published in one. Knowing how much these weekly publications are valued is what inspired me to write for the short story market long before my first novel.

When are you happiest?
When I'm reading or with my husband Michael, and our dog, Henry. Most days I'm working on my latest novel in my own little world but now that my husband has retired, we can walk Henry or drive to a garden centre or National Trust property.

If you could go back in time, which era would you choose?
The 1930s and 1940s to experience life as it was then. The house we lived in when first married was built in 1902 and is also Ruby's house in my *Woolworths* series of books. We lived there for over

twenty years and I imagine Ruby and her family sitting in what was my front room.

What makes you mad?
The bad breeding of dogs. If I were Prime Minister for a day I'd close down every puppy farm and back yard breeder in the UK. The RSPCA and Government do not do enough to shut down puppy farms.

Any childhood holiday memories?
The late sixties hold many memories of trips to Warners' Holiday Camps on the Isle of Wight and Great Yarmouth. No doubt this is why I was so keen to set one of my books, *The Butlins Girls*, in the hey day of such wonderful places.

What is your favourite novel or film?
I wanted to be Jo in *Little Women* and sit in the attic writing. The film I can watch again and again is *This Happy Breed* by Noel Coward.
Find more favourites by authors and staff throughout the Annual!

Christmas at Woolworths takes us to the end of 1945 when the girls face the future now the war is over.

FANCY THAT!

Fascinating Facts **On Wheels!**

✦ At first cars were seen as the "green" alternative transport because horses were causing so much pollution with their poop!

✦ Mrs G Duncan was the first woman bus conductor in London, with the Thomas Tilling Company on route 37.

✦ 1974 saw Jill Viner as London Transport's first woman bus driver.

✦ China has the biggest bus. The Neoplan Jumbo Cruiser has three sections (to allow it to turn corners) with five doors, can carry 300 people and is 82 feet long!

✦ As early as 1662 Blaise Pascal operated the first horse-drawn omnibus in Paris – but due to high ticket costs it only ran for 15 years.

✦ The word bus is an abbreviation of "omnibus", which is Latin for "for all", as they are transport for all people.

✦ Electric cars are not a new thing; they were already being manufactured in 1905 but fell out of favour by 1920 when the gas-combustion engine became cheaper to run.

✦ In 1965 Barbara Castle became the first woman Minister for Transport.

Before 1907, London buses were different colours to signify their route

✦ The Knight Bus, seen in the film *Harry Potter and the Prisoner of Azkaban,* was constructed using three RT-class AEC Regent III buses.

✦ Waterloo Bridge was completed in 1945 and is nicknamed "Ladies Bridge" because of the predominantly female workforce who built it.

Elf

It's a stressful job – especially for
someone whose heart has just been broken...

By Steve Beresford

Queen were singing *Thank God
It's Christmas* over the speakers
as Lucy Pelham shepherded
mostly excited children and less excited
adults past the two nodding reindeer. And
this was when Carl Grenville turned up.

"This way to the grotto, everyone!"
Lucy was saying. "Not long now until
you see Santa."

"Santa ain't real!" one boy said. "S'all
just made up!"

This prompted the girl behind him to
immediately start snivelling.

"What's he mean, no Santa?"

"Of course there's a Santa," Lucy said.

"En't!" A stamped foot.

"Everybody knows there's a Santa.
You'll see him in a…" Lucy suddenly
spotted Carl. "Oh heck."

Carl was standing next to the grinning
snowman. He waved.

"Lucy!"

Unwillingly Lucy extricated herself
from the grotto queue.

"Carl." She made sure her feelings
were known just by the way she
pronounced his name.

"Don't be like that."

"I thought I made it clear I didn't want
to see you again."

Over the speakers Mud began singing
It'll Be Lonely This Christmas.

"I can explain." He stepped over the
low fence surrounding the grotto and
started towards her.

"You can't come in here," she told him.
"Not unless you want to see Santa."

"I want to see you. Can we go
somewhere else? More private? To talk?"

Santa's Winter Wonderland was on the
ground floor of the Spires Shopping
Centre in Chilfield, near the main doors.
Christmas songs were fighting to be heard
over the general hubbub of three
interlinked floors of seasonally-affected
shoppers. And the line of excited children
outside the grotto was constant.

Lucy chewed her lip and automatically
rubbed at her now ring-less finger.

Carl noticed. "Ah, you've taken it off."

"What did you expect?"

The engagement ring was safe at her
sister's house – retrieved after being
hurled across the room – and Lucy felt a
mixture of regret, disappointment and
anger. She was also acutely aware of the
queue watching her.

"Holly, could you cover for me?" she

asked, turning to her colleague.

Holly said that yes, she would.

"Holly?" queried Carl as Lucy led him away through the shop.

"Yes, so?"

"Holly? At Christmas?"

"Her sister's working here too. Ivy."

"Ivy?" Carl snorted in disbelief. "Holly and Ivy?"

"And there's Carol too." Lucy pointed and Carol waved.

"You'll be telling me next," Carl said, "that Santa is really a man called Noel."

"It's Roger, actually. Roger Festive."

"Oh, now come on. You've got to be kid…" Carl stopped as his eyes made a circuit of her body. "Phoo-wee," he whispered as though noticing her clothes for the first time. "Now that's what I call an outfit."

"I'm an elf." Lucy's outfit consisted of a red and green tunic, a matching mini-skirt, striped tights and pixie shoes. And a hat. With a feather in it and a tinkly bell.

"An elf, eh?" He grinned. "Very nice."

Lucy took his arm and dragged him further away from the grotto.

"Don't," she snapped. "Not in front of the children." She circled the massive Christmas tree which towered into the central atrium of the shopping centre and stopped on the opposite side to the grotto to give them some privacy.

"I was looking for you upstairs," Carl said. "They said you were down here at the grotto. They didn't mention you were dressed as an elf."

"I volunteered."

Well, she'd been press-ganged. Lucy usually worked up in the shopping centre's admin department, but one of the **Continued overleaf**

Continued from previous page
original elves had been removed from duty. Mary Snow's rather generous natural assets had proved too much for her tight tunic and she had been literally bursting with Christmas spirit.

Management had stepped in quickly and hurried Mary back upstairs when she started trending on social media for all the wrong reasons. Her outfit had been handed to the rather less curvy Lucy.

Lucy hadn't known whether to be insulted or not when she failed to ignite a Twitter firestorm of her own.

"Anyway," Carl said, "I'm not here to talk about elves and Santa. I'm here to say you're being ridiculous and you should give me another chance to explain."

"And why should I do that?"

"Because it's Christmas. Because it's the season of goodwill to all men." He tried to gaze meaningfully. "Because I love you." He only succeeded in looking like he desperately needed the loo.

Even so, Lucy Pelham's heart danced a

Superglued to Carl's, judging by the time it took them to break apart.

Lucy had stormed out, gone to her sister's overnight and left her phone switched off.

"It wasn't me!" Carl protested, as over the speakers *I Saw Mommy Kissing Santa Claus* struck up.

"Then it was someone doing an extremely good impersonation of you."

"Well, obviously it was me. What I mean is, it wasn't my fault."

"You were kissing her."

"No. She was kissing me."

"Is there a difference?"

"A very big difference, actually."

"Not from where I was standing."

"I wasn't even aware there was mistletoe above me."

"No, of course not."

"I wasn't!" Carl slapped a hand to his forehead in frustration. "I was merely crossing the office to talk to Jack when Maxine Pritchard suddenly leapt out of nowhere and attacked me."

"You're being ridiculous and you should give me another chance to explain"

merry jig against her ribs. But then the image of Carl with that other woman flashed across her mind, and the jig became a limping stumble.

"Maybe you should have thought of that last night."

It had been Carl's office Christmas party. Lucy had turned up unexpectedly to surprise him. Unfortunately, she'd found him under a sprig of mistletoe, in the tight embrace of a pretty blonde. The woman's lips had apparently been

"Attacked you?" Lucy snorted.

"Yes, attacked me. She launched herself like a ninja assassin, saying something about a kiss for Maxie under the mistletoe. Before I even knew what was happening she was devouring my face. Which was when you walked in."

"How thoughtless of me."

"Don't you trust me?"

Of course she trusted him! He was Carl Grenville. She was engaged to marry him. She loved him. So why, oh why couldn't she shift the image of his kiss with Maxine Pritchard from her mind – and why did it make her feel so icky inside?

"Right, I have proof." Carl produced his smartphone from a pocket and began poking the screen. "Here, look at these." He thrust the phone into Lucy's hand.

Lucy looked at the screen. It showed a picture of the same woman – Maxine – kissing another man.

"Look at the next picture. And the next. And the next."

Lucy looked at seven pictures in all. Of Maxine kissing seven different men. Two were clearly enjoying it. Two looked surprised. Two looked terrified. The final one looked unconscious. Maybe he'd suffocated midway through the onslaught.

"See?" said Carl. "It was some bet she'd had with Zoe. How many men could she kiss under the mistletoe? Zoe was snapping pictures and they were going to put them on the office noticeboard. When I found out, I got her to send me some." He shuffled nervously. "Obviously I deleted the one with me in it. I thought you wouldn't want to see that again."

"No, I wouldn't."

"So am I forgiven? Not that I have anything to be forgiven for. I was the innocent party, after all."

Lucy thought about it. She should have known all along that there had to be an explanation. But she'd gone off at the deep end, as she often did. It was a failing, she knew, but her emotions did get the better of her occasionally.

She handed his phone back. "Can you forgive me?" She held up her hand and pointed at her ring-less finger.

He adopted that silly puppy-dog expression he did so well.

"There's nothing to forgive." He took her hand and kissed the finger. "Just as long as you didn't flush the ring, or anything like that. It cost a fortune, that did."

Over the speakers John Lennon began singing *Happy Xmas (War Is Over)*.

"Oh Carl!"

"Oh Lucy!"

They embraced and kissed – and then Carl suddenly pointed towards the automatic doors.

"Hey, look, it's snowing!"

Thick white flakes were already starting to blanket the busy pavement outside.

"Perfect," Lucy said, meaning the snow, meaning Carl, meaning basically everything.

"By the way, this elf outfit…" Carl grinned, his eyebrows twitching. "Do you get to take it home?"

Lucy giggled. Oh yes, this might be the most perfect Christmas ever.

• •

MY FAVOURITE…

My favourite TV show was *Ghostwatch* by Stephen Volk (1992)… Clever writing, scary visual tricks and a terrifying climax, this faux live documentary was television at its very best.

Mr Postman...

It's never too late to send that Christmas card you now know you should have sent many decades ago

By Alma Harris

J immy O'Reilly loved me. I know this because he wrote it in my Christmas card when I was ten.

I was fond of him, of course. I liked it when we met coming home from our respective schools and he carried my satchel. I was touched when he gave me 2/6d for my eleventh birthday, but I accepted it rather as a princess might accept homage from one of her knights.

much to play, but we went to the same school and travelled home on the same bus. She kept me up to date with all the family news and I listened more intently whenever she spoke of Patrick.

He knew he was handsome, she said, and he went through girls like footballers went through through socks. But I thought that once he properly met me, he would never seek another.

I was fifteen when they started the youth club and I went along because I

He was handsome and went through girls like footballers went through socks

The truth is that he wasn't my favourite. There were a great many O'Reillys and Patrick, his older brother, was the one to whom I wanted to give my favour.

Patrick was everything Jimmy wasn't; handsome in a cool Irish sort of way, with wavy hair the colour of soot and eyes blue as the cobalt in my paintbox. Jimmy had straight brown hair, greyish eyes and a complexion muddied by freckles.

Mary O'Reilly was my friend. She was Jimmy's twin, and usually harnessed to hassle all the younger O'Reillys into church on a Sunday or into some harmless occupation while Mrs O'Reilly sorted the household. She wasn't available

was a girl and there were going to be boys. And because Patrick was one of them. It was late summer and I wore a turquoise sundress my mother made. I was never beautiful, but that evening I believed I was.

Patrick must have thought so too because he brought me out for a smoke – his habit, not mine – and steered me round the back of the hall. It was already twilight and we stood in the light spilling out from the kitchenette. He kissed me, then again as we lay on the grass.

But I wouldn't.

Girls didn't then, most of them. We all knew those who had, the ones who went away and suddenly acquired a "little

sister", the ones who went away and cried for the babies they'd lost and the rare ones who faced it out and were forever pointed at.

Patrick had the good grace to escort me back inside but then left me for the snooker table.

I saw Jimmy look at him and then at me, but he must have already decided that I was after bigger fish. After all, I was doing French and Latin and he was going to be a plumber.

There were exams then and college,

and I met Harry and finally stopped looking for love because I'd found it.

Mary kept me informed of all the local happenings… who married who, what careers they were making, how many children they had. Patrick couldn't settle, she said, but Jimmy was getting married. She'd been nursing in Ireland but their parents were ailing and she'd had to come home.

Later her letters were full of Jimmy and how he was in such demand. He'd
Continued overleaf

Continued from previous page

won the Town Hall plumbing contract and now everybody who was anybody wanted him to fix their taps. Who'd have thought it, he was an actual employer with two apprentices. Just think, she said, as soon as Colm comes of age he's planning to be O'Reilly and Son.

She was strangely silent about Patrick. Gradually the news filtered through.

grandmother used to say. For me these days, handsome means strength and kindness and courage, and I have learned to recognise these qualities.

Jimmy thanks me for coming. His hair is also grey but a softer grey and his eyes have creases in the corners, weathered from hard work.

As we pick at sandwiches and sausage rolls and I am at the end of the queue for

For me, these days, handsome means strength, kindness, courage

I'd gathered most of the facts by the time it hit the nationals. Patrick was guilty of fraud – some timeshare scheme – and his victims were all women. The courageous ones allowed their pictures to be shown. They were stunning, as I expected.

All that seems only five minutes ago, but today here I am at Mary's funeral, a widow myself.

I can see Patrick in front of me, charm lying on him like wax on a lemon. He has steel-grey hair and I imagine his eyes are still as blue as ever, his skin as smooth as if ironed by arrogance.

It should be him remembering his little sister but it's Jimmy on the podium, talking about Mary and sometimes having to stop. It's Jimmy, too, who has made all the arrangements and chosen the wicker coffin garlanded with cream and yellow roses. He no longer has his wife to support him but he carries the responsibility without flinching.

As we leave and Patrick shakes my hand, I feel absolutely nothing. "Handsome is as handsome does," my

tea, I see him bringing me a cup.

"Do you remember when I used to carry your satchel?" he asks.

I am grateful for the chair he finds me and the time it gives me to reply.

"I used your two-and-six for a hardback notebook to write my poems in," I say.

"I know. I knew everything about you." He is smiling at the recollection.

"I was quite cruel then, and very stupid." My voice is almost a whisper.

"No," he says, "we were very young."

When I leave he holds me gently and kisses me on both my cheeks. Jimmy O'Reilly loves me still.

And now I know at last that I love Jimmy O'Reilly and always will – and tomorrow I shall write the Christmas card to tell him so.

. . . .

MY FAVOURITE...

My favourite film is *Some Like It Hot*, with Marilyn Monroe, Tony Curtis and Jack Lemmon – simply because it always makes me laugh.

Brain BOOSTERS

Codeword

Each letter of the alphabet has been replaced by a number.
The numbers for the first name of our chosen celebrity are given.
Dakota Johnson is the daughter of which famous parents?

A B C D E F G H I J K L M N O P Q R S T U V W X Y Z

| 1 | 2 | 3 T | 4 | 5 | 6 O | 7 | 8 | 9 | 10 | 11 | 12 | 13 |
| 14 A | 15 K | 16 | 17 | 18 D | 19 | 20 | 21 | 22 | 23 | 24 | 25 | 26 |

Turn To Page 143 For Solutions

| 2 | 12 | 20 | 14 A | 8 | 4 | 12 | | 10 | 23 | 4 | 13 | 13 | 4 | 3 T | 9 |

| 14 A | 8 | 18 | 18 D | 6 D | 8 O | | 21 | 6 O | 9 | 8 | 16 | 6 O | 8 |

The Christmas Angel

The girl in the shop window was a vision of loveliness – but would he ever meet her in the real world?

By Rosemary Hayes

Jacob

As Jacob walked down the road, something caught his eye in the shop window: a life-size angel. She was a vision in white placing a shining star on top of a snow-laden Christmas tree. At first he thought the angel was part of the store's Christmas display. Then she moved.

Jacob stared, entranced. Sensing his presence, she turned and smiled at him. A smile that touched his heart.

He wanted to go inside and say hello, but he was already late for work. Reluctantly, he left the window.

Sitting at his desk later, he struggled to concentrate on the numbers on his computer screen.

"Jacob, are you daydreaming?"

His boss's voice snapped him out of his thoughts.

"No, sorry… what's up, Mr Peters?"

"I need you to put together a report for the 1pm manager meeting. OK?"

"Sure." Since he was late this morning "no" wasn't an option. There went his hope of seeing the angel in his lunchbreak.

Tracey

Tracey enjoyed creating the window displays. Today she was building an elves' toy factory with wooden models and decorations. To stay in theme, she wore an elf costume, complete with pointy ears.

At first she had found it a little embarrassing wearing the costumes while she decorated the windows, but then she noticed the enjoyment people walking past seemed to get from it. Children would wave, adults' faces would light up – and then there was that cute guy who had stopped at the window yesterday.

His expression had made her breath catch and she had smiled at him instantly. There was something about him that made her heartbeat speed up, but then he hurried off. Whatever had passed between them must have only been in her imagination.

Maybe the thought of being alone this year, with no family nearby, and her closest friends away, had made her see something that just wasn't there.

She shook herself. She'd probably never see him again.

Continued overleaf

Sweet

Continued from previous page

Jacob

She looked adorable today, in her elf costume. He had only been looking in the window a moment when she turned and noticed him standing there.

Her smile was radiant and it made his heart thump against his ribs. Was she pleased to see him again, or was it only wishful thinking? He pointed to the elf toyshop display and gave a thumbs up.

"Both," he admitted.

Tracey

"That's nice to hear," said Tracey. The man whirled round, surprise on his face.

"Hi… Tracey," he said. "I'm Jacob."

"I saw you head inside, and thought it might be easier to have a conversation without a glass pane between us."

"I've never seen anything so lovely before," he told the lady at the till

Looks great, he mouthed.

Thank you, she mouthed back.

He pointed to his ears and then her pointy ears. *Very cute.*

She laughed and pointed at him. Did she just say, *very cute too?* He wanted to believe she did, but a conversation through glass isn't the easiest thing in the world.

He checked his watch, then headed inside the store. Only then did he realise he couldn't speak to her from this side. The window was totally enclosed. A small door led to the inside of the window scene, but it was off limits to customers.

He headed to the closest cash register.

"Excuse me," he said to the lady standing there. "Your Christmas window displays look fantastic."

"Thanks. Yes, Tracey's doing a wonderful job. We're receiving lots of positive feedback."

Tracey. At least now he had a name.

"I'm not surprised. I've never seen anything so lovely before."

"Are you talking about the Christmas windows, or Tracey herself?"

"A lot easier." He smiled. "I um… this sounds corny, but I couldn't stop thinking about you after I saw you yesterday."

Whatever nerves she felt melted away, like snow under the summer sun.

"That's a coincidence," she said. "I couldn't stop thinking about you either."

"I work at the accountants on Mary Street. I don't suppose you'd be free for lunch today?"

"That sounds lovely."

She changed out of the costume before they met for lunch. From the moment they sat down their conversation flowed and it felt she had known him for years. Funny how things can change in only one lunch hour. She found herself looking forward to Christmas after all.

• •

MY FAVOURITE…

My favourite book is *Lord Of The Rings* by J R R Tolkien. It was the first novel I had ever read that left me wishing that the world within the pages was actually real.

Trio Of Tiny Tartlets

Ingredients (Serves 4)

- **12 small savoury pastry cases**
- **3tbsp crème fraîche or soft cheese**
- **80g hot smoked salmon, flaked**
- **Lemon slices, capers and dill, to garnish**
- **½ small avocado, mashed**
- **Cherry tomato quarters and basil, to garnish**
- **2tbsp soured cream**
- **2tbsp grated beetroot (vacuum packed, not in vinegar)**
- **Sliced radish, gherkins and parsley sprigs, to garnish**

1 Put 3 pastry cases onto each of 4 serving plates. Put 1 heaped tsp of crème fraîche or soft cheese into 4 tartlets, and top with flakes of salmon. Garnish with lemon, capers and dill.

2 Mix the remaining crème fraîche or soft cheese with the avocado and spoon this into 4 more tartlets. Garnish with cherry tomato and basil.

3 Mix most of the soured cream with the beetroot. Spoon this into the remaining 4 tartlets. Top with the remaining soured cream, then garnish with radish, gherkins and parsley sprigs.

RECIPE AND FOOD STYLING: SUE ASHWORTH PHOTOGRAPHY JONATHAN SHORT

Better Than A Flannelette Nightie

Paul has a very special reason to break the habit of thirty years of marriage and go shopping...

by **Norman Kitching**

J ean deftly closed the front door behind her with one foot, using the two handfuls of shopping bags to help her balance on the other. She dropped the bags in the middle of the hall, staggered into the kitchen and flopped onto a chair.

"Finished!" she declared with a sigh.

"You or the Christmas shopping?" asked her husband, Paul, as he poured boiling water into the teapot.

"Both, I think. Honestly, I'm sure the shops get busier every year."

served up, because they were traditional.

In the same way, she thought she could always be sure that Paul would never do any Christmas shopping. Now, after thirty years of marriage, he was claiming to have broken the rule

"Don't sound so surprised," he said, in a rather hurt tone. "I had a couple of very special presents to buy this year."

He poured the tea and took his cup through to the sitting room, leaving Jean to wonder, rather nervously, what Christmas surprise was in store for her.

She and Paul had never spent large amounts on Christmas presents for each

Paul never got involved in buying presents – he knew his limitations

"Yes," replied Paul, casually. "I noticed how crowded it was everywhere when I did my Christmas shopping yesterday."

Jean's jaw dropped.

"I don't believe you just said that. You? Christmas shopping?"

In Jean's experience there were a number of unwritten rules about Christmas. For instance, it was a racing certainty that nobody would eat more than two sprouts each on Christmas Day even though they all insisted they were

other. This was something they agreed on at the very start of their married life, out of practical sense rather than meanness.

Money was never plentiful and there was always something else to spend it on. In the early days the house took most of their spare cash, for furniture or decorating.

Then the kids came along, so there wasn't much left for Mum and Dad. Christmas presents for them were restricted to sensible, useful items.

"Goodness me," Paul would say in

mock surprise. "Some new underpants. What a brilliant idea."

"Well, look what Santa's brought me," Jean would reply. "How did he know this is my favourite bath soap?"

The kids would nudge each other and giggle. "They say that every year." Each year, every single present Santa brought would be selected and purchased on his behalf by Jean. Paul never got involved in the process – though he was quite happy to foot the bill, knowing that Jean would be sensible. He also knew his limitations.

Only once did he attempt to buy a Christmas present for Jean. That was the first Christmas after their wedding, and Jean smiled at the memory.

Luckily Paul's sister got involved at the last minute or Santa would have brought Jean a bright red flannelette nightie.

Jean's reminiscing was interrupted by another bombshell from Paul.

"Have we any wrapping paper, love?"

Not only did Paul never do any Christmas shopping, he never did any of the wrapping, either. He was useless at it.

"There's a couple of rolls on top of the wardrobe in the back bedroom," replied a shell-shocked Jean.

The idea of two spare rolls of paper lying around amused her. Once upon a time, Christmas wrapping paper was carefully recycled from one year to the next. Thanks to *Blue Peter*, the kids made their own cards and decorations.

It all helped to save money, but now things were easier. The mortgage was paid off, the kids' educations were completed and they'd all left home.

As Jean sipped her tea, she looked around the kitchen and realised that this had been the first year ever that they'd had a bit of money to spare.

It'd been wisely spent, of course, on
Continued overleaf

improvements to the house including a nice new kitchen which Paul had promised would be finished by Christmas. Even so, there were one or two gaps that were worrying Jean.

She went back to wondering about the special presents that Paul said he bought yesterday. Since he was also wrapping them himself, they were obviously meant to be a big surprise.

What had he bought her? A bottle of expensive perfume, the sort that supermarkets didn't sell? A gold ring that didn't look as if it had been won at a fairground? A piece of jewellery that wasn't in a catalogue shop?

"It's no use, love," said Paul, interrupting her dreams. "Can you do me a favour and wrap this up, please?"

Jean stared in disbelief at the Rubik's Cube on the kitchen table in front of her.

"Please tell me that this is not a Christmas present for me, otherwise you're in big trouble."

"Don't be silly. It's for Ginny."

"Do you mean our twenty-eight-year-old daughter, Ginny? The one who is married with two children?"

Paul smiled and nodded.

"She asked for one in her letter – the one I found up the chimney. I'll get it."

Paul had obviously not improved with age. If a Rubik's Cube was his idea of a special present for Ginny, she didn't dare think what he might have bought for her.

Paul returned and handed her a grubby piece of paper.

"I found it when I opened up the fireplace in the sitting room. Ginny must have slid it under the plasterboard. Years ago, judging by the handwriting."

"*Dear Santa,*" Jean read out loud. "*Please can I have a Rubik's Cube for Christmas as I am the only girl at school who hasn't got one. Love, Ginny.*"

"She never did have a Rubik's Cube," said Paul. "So I thought it would fun to buy her one now. It took me ages to find one."

"That's all very well, but what worries me is the second part." Jean continued to read it out.

"*PS. Mummy needs a new thing to do the washing up with. She calls it a dish mop. Her other one is all worn out.*" She glared at Paul. "*Don't* tell me you've bought me a dish mop for Christmas."

"Don't be daft," said Paul, smiling broadly. "We can afford to do better than that now, love. A brand new dishwasher arrives tomorrow. I've left a space for it in the kitchen."

Jean gave Paul a great big hug. She knew he'd never change, and she wouldn't want him to.

A dishwasher, she thought. *How very romantic!*

Still, she reminded herself, it was a good deal more life-enhancing than a flannelette nightie.

MY FAVOURITE...

My favourite book is *A Tale of Two Cities* by Charles Dickens. Although terrible things happen, it's populated by such wonderful characters.
Sally Hampton, Editor-in-Chief

Brain BOOSTERS

Kriss Kross

Try to fit all the listed words back into the grid.

Turn To Page 143 For Solutions

4 letters
Kerb
Kite
Nark
Taut
Tidy
Tuba

5 letters
Douse
Gassy
Slake
Vouch
Yeast

6 letters
Emigre
Grovel
Native
Ragbag

7 letters
Dustpan
Forlorn
Raddled
Statute

8 letters
Division
Goatskin
Redouble
Stretchy

Meant To Be

Was it puppy love, or could it grow into so much more?

By Tess Niland Kimber

J enna stood in the shop flicking through the cards. There wasn't anything decent left in the racks. It was her own fault; she'd left it too late to shop for Valentine's Day cards, but she'd had good reason not to buy earlier.

The first card she picked up was too pink, the second too jokey, and this one from the back was illustrated with golf clubs and a fishing rod!

She sighed. In a couple of hours, she was meeting Nick at The Captain's Table, their favourite gastro pub.

"Shall I collect you?" he'd asked, calling out of the blue, yesterday.

"Um… no, I'll see you there," she'd said, trying to sense his mood from his tone. Was it warm? Distant? Hopeful?

It was only after she'd ended the call that she remembered the date – February 14th. Their latest row had meant they'd spent the last week apart. Why was he suddenly asking her out on Valentine's Day? Had he, too, forgotten the date?

Maybe he wanted to beg for forgiveness and move back in? Or, perhaps, he was planning to end their relationship once and for all. Surely, he wouldn't be that cruel – dumping her on the most romantic day of the year!

She bit her lip. Should she be excited or worried?

Unable to guess, she decided to treat it as a date. She'd wear her new red dress and give him the perfect card when they met at The Captain's Table. It was so important she get this right, that the evening went well…

J enna had first met Nick at work. Well, technically that wasn't true. She'd been working when Nick came into the practice with Milo, his golden retriever.

"There's something stuck in his paw," he'd said, worry ghosting his brown eyes.

Jenna had helped him lift the dog onto her examining table, trying to ignore the owner and concentrate on his pet. Normally it wasn't a problem, but there was something about Nick that immediately fascinated her.

After breaking up with her last boyfriend she'd hoped she was immune to men, especially good looking ones, but Nick caught her off-guard. Why? Was it his tangle of curly brown hair? Or his wide smile? Or those velvety eyes?

No, she decided, as he stroked Milo's head and whispered to calm him, it was his natural kindness and obvious love for his dog. For an animal lover like Jenna, there couldn't be a more attractive quality in a man.

As she'd examined Milo's paw, he'd tried to drag it away, like a frightened child. "It's a thorn," she'd said. "I'll soon get it out. Please, could you hold Milo?"

"Certainly." Nick had smiled.

She'd removed it in no time, then treated the wound with antiseptic spray.

"Keep it clean and dry and Milo should be fine in a few days. Are his jabs up to date?" she asked, unashamedly inventing a reason for his return.

"Oh, yes."

Her spirits plummeted.

But she needn't have worried. Nick and Milo became regular visitors to the practice – coming along on weaker and weaker pretences each time. It only took her a couple of weeks to work out that Nick was just as interested in her as she was in him.

Eventually he did ask her out. Not on a date as such – just a joint dog walk in the park. Luckily, her springer spaniel Pepper took to Milo as much as they did to each other. Seamlessly, they moved from vet and client to dog-walkers, then to boyfriend and girlfriend.

"I've never known you fall for a man so quickly," Claire, her assistant at practice, claimed. "I thought your ideal partner would have fur and four legs."

Jenna had laughed.

"I think it's because Nick loves animals as much as I do."

And while they'd only touched on the subject of marriage, the idea of joint kennels for Milo and Pepper, at either of their homes, was raised several times. Eventually Nick moved in to her cottage.

That was when their troubles began…

Painfully conscious that she would soon be meeting Nick and she still hadn't found the perfect Valentine's Day card, Jenna dashed to another shop further down the High Street.

Frantically rifling through their selection, she finally found what she was looking for and smiled. Here was just the right card! The picture was ideal and the **Continued overleaf** words said everything she wanted to say. Could it possibly work magic and heal their relationship?

After a few months, moving in together had felt like a natural step.

"My house would be best," she'd suggested. "It's near both our workplaces and the bigger garden would be great for Milo and Pepper."

"Sorted!" Nick had smiled.

The move went smoothly. Nick had found a tenant for his flat almost as soon as the ink was dry on the advert. He'd packed all his worldly goods – a tennis racket, sizeable CD collection and several M&S suits – and moved in over the course their strengthening relationship in front of a flickering log fire.

Could she be any happier? Jenna had wondered, gazing into his eyes.

But as the days passed their different "parenting" of the dogs became obvious.

"No, Nick!" Jenna shouted, walking into the kitchen one Sunday afternoon to find him crouched by the dogs, teaching them to sit on command. Every time they succeeded he gave them a treat. "Please, don't feed Pepper biscuits."

He'd looked up, amazed by her sharp tone. "I was only rewarding them. Milo loves biscuits."

"So does Pepper, and it's taken me months to wean her off them."

He hadn't argued but shrugged,

What had brought them together quickly began to drive them apart – their dogs

of one weekend. Everything was perfect… except that what had brought them together quickly began driving them apart – their dogs.

"Milo – down, boy," Jenna had said to the golden retriever on the first evening Nick moved into her cottage.

The dog was sprawled on her leather sofa as if it was his throne.

"Sorry, Jen… he's used to curling up on my sofa at the flat. It doesn't matter, does it?"

"Well, I don't let Pepper on the furniture. And besides, you've got me to cuddle now." She'd curled her arms around his waist, reaching up to kiss him.

That initial reprimand had been soon forgotten. Later they'd shared mushroom risotto with a bottle of white wine to toast looking a little put out – and as disappointed as Pepper when he'd put the tasty treats away.

This had been the start of the wedge that grew between them. Nick's idea of dog care was totally at odds with Jenna's.

"I don't think either of us are wrong, we just have different approaches," she'd confided to Claire as they sat in the staff room one wet lunchtime.

"It was like that with me and Pete."

"But you don't have a dog," she'd frowned, sipping her hot drink.

"No, but I tore my hair out when we first got together. His way of dealing with the children was the exact opposite to how I handled them. He'd let Laura do things I'd never allow Jasmine to do. It led to a lot of friction in the early months."

Claire's words had put Jenna's mind at rest – until she'd arrived home, after a particularly frantic clinic, to find her new lingerie had been chewed to pieces! Why had Nick let Milo into their bedroom with access to her belongings?

"It's not good enough!" she'd raged, holding up unrecognisable scraps of pink silk.

This time Nick had actively argued back.

"Milo and I have lived happily together for three years. If you don't like it, then perhaps we'd better move out," he'd shouted.

"Fine!" she'd said, instantly regretting it as sadness crept into his eyes.

That had been a week ago. She'd heard on the grapevine that Nick and Milo, unable to return to his flat as it was let for the next four months, were sofa surfing at various friend's homes.

"It's silly – you love each other," Claire said. "Just pick up the phone and apologise. Agree some ground rules for the kids – I mean, dogs – and move on."

"You're right," she said, already excited by the idea of a reunion. But before she could call him, Nick had rung, asking to meet at The Captain's Table.

Was he going to ask to come back? Or had he decided their different approaches to dog ownership highlighted significant problems in their relationship? Was he about to make their separation permanent?

The Captain's Table was a beautiful old-fashioned pub, renowned for its food. Crouched under a mane of gingered thatch, the low whitewashed building was at the base of a lane that snaked, like a black river, through bordering fields.

Jenna held her breath, watching the signboard swaying in the breeze as memories rushed at her. Last time they'd visited was on their first date. It had been cold and damp, autumn at its dreariest.

That evening they'd parked beside the willow tree. As she had climbed out of the car, the belt of her coat had become trapped in the door. Discreetly, she'd tried to extract it.

"Come here," Nick had said, huskily.

She'd closed her eyes as, with strong man-rubs, he'd brushed wet grit from her coat – and love into her heart.

Walking towards the pub now, she remembered how charming he'd been then, opening the door for her.

"It's a dog-friendly pub," he'd told her. "We must bring Milo and Pepper one day."

He was always thinking about the dogs and she'd loved that. How she had longed for him to sweep her into his arms, but back then she'd been playing the cool game with the main rule, *Don't show your feelings too soon.*

Pushing open the door now, she saw red heart-shaped balloons clinging to the oak beams. Sitting at tables lit by candles were loving couples.

She felt a tingle of discomfort. Did Nick

Continued overleaf

really think this was the right backdrop to announce a permanent split? Or could she dare hope they'd soon be back together?

The Valentine's Day card safely in her handbag, she searched the dining area. There he was – sitting in the far corner.

It was too late for "cool" now – she was in love with him.

"Jenna," he breathed, rising to his feet.

The log fire flickered, casting orange shadows on Nick as he walked toward her.

Her fears that their relationship was over slipped away when she saw the love reflected in his eyes.

"Nick, I'm…"

He touched a finger to her lips before leading her to their table.

"Let's talk later. I've missed you, Jen."

"Me, too."

Incongruous to the horse brasses and flagstone floor, *Chasing Cars* by Snow Patrol was playing in the background, the lyrics making her feel overwhelmed with emotion. How she would love to just lie in his arms and forget the world, to cross that divide between them.

"Jen, I'm so sorry. It was stupid to fall out over the dogs."

She reached across the table, lacing her fingers through his.

"No, it was my fault. I shouldn't have been so… so bossy."

He grinned. "This is mad – now we're arguing over who should apologise."

"It's Valentine's Day… we shouldn't disagree over anything."

Before she could reach into her handbag for the card, he handed her a single red rose. "It's a bit cheesy but…"

"Oh no, Nick – it's romantic."

"And this is for you, too," he said and gave her a gift bag. But when she went to open it, he put out a steadying hand.

"I wouldn't… not here…"

She frowned – until she saw the La Perla lingerie logo printed on the side.

"It's to replace the set Milo ruined."

"Why, if I didn't know you better, I'd think you were blushing! Thank you, Nick. I've something for you, too – although not as exciting as this."

Smiling, she gave him the card.

"I hate being without you – and so does Milo," he said, opening the envelope. He grinned when he saw the card's illustration. It showed two dogs, looking remarkably like Milo and Pepper, snuggled up together. "This is great, Jen. Thank you."

"Look, I've been thinking… I won't be so strict with the dogs in future. Live and let live, and all that. Nothing's worth us splitting up over."

He smiled. "And I've been thinking, too. Perhaps Milo could do with some obedience classes."

Compromise, Jenna thought, sniffing her red rose. It didn't sound as romantic as the word *love* or *Valentine* but, in the great scheme of things, it was probably just as important.

"So are you coming home?"

"Try and stop me – Milo, too!"

He laughed, reaching across the table to kiss her.

This, Jenna thought, would be a Valentine's Day to remember – always.

• •

MY FAVOURITE...

My favourite film is *The Piano*. Everyone should hold out for someone who looks at them with as much emotion in their eyes as George Baines has for Holly Hunter's character, Ada.

FANCY THAT!

Fascinating Facts **On Tracks!**

✦ **The London Underground opened in 1863 and was the first underground in the world, with steam engines running for 4 miles along the Metropolitan line.**

✦ It's possible to travel from Portugal to Vietnam solely by train, and at 17,000km it's the longest train journey in the world.

✦ **High speed trains typically create less air pollution than a plane over the same distance.**

✦ In Japan, trains are so punctual that a delay of over 5 minutes incurs an apology and a "delay certificate" for passengers to present to their employers. A delay of an hour or more may even make the news!

✦ **Ann Dodds was the first female train operator on the London Underground in 1978.**

✦ During WWI the number of women working on the railways rose from 9,000 to 50,000.

Currently only 20% of people working in rail are women

✦ There are 40,000 bridges and tunnels, 9,000 level crossings, and 9,941 miles of railway tracks in Britain's rail network.

The fight scene on top of a train in *Skyfall* was filmed on a real moving train – and Daniel Craig did not use a stunt double.

Mother Love

Little Millie was so lovely, she was worth every single minute of lost sleep for doting Ellie…

By Della Galton

E llie opened her eyes as the wailing started up again in the bedroom just across the landing. Beside her, Nick rolled over and yawned.

"I'll go," he mumbled.

"It's OK, it's my turn."

Swallowing her tiredness, Ellie sat up and swung her legs over the side of the bed. She felt for her slippers, slightly to the right of the dressing table, grabbed her robe from the door and shrugged it on. She could do all this stuff in her sleep…

"It's a pity *you're* not asleep, young lady," she told Millicent Angela Collins (Millie for short), as she scooped her out of her cot. "Are you wet, sweetheart?"

Millie looked at her wide-eyed.

"No, you're not, are you? Hungry, then?"

Downstairs, she warmed a bottle. Then she carried the baby over to the cane rocking chair by the window, her slippers flapping on the conservatory tiles.

Curled up in the chair with Ellie a warm bundle in her arms, she began to feed her. Millie spat out the teat after three seconds and waved her tiny arms crossly.

"So it's just cuddles then, is it, darling? Well, cuddles are good."

She began to rock and hum very softly. Millie loved it when she hummed. Her gaze fixed on Ellie's face and then very slowly her eyelids began to droop. Rock and hum. Rock and hum.

In the blackness beyond the garden Ellie could see that the sky was beginning to lighten, a soft swirl above the trees. Their garden backed on to fields. Once when she'd been sitting here in the darkness she'd seen an owl swoop low across the grass.

It was amazing how much nocturnal activity there was if you were around to see it. Pity that meant she was usually too bleary-eyed to see straight in the morning. She was getting way too old for nights without sleep. Not that she was complaining.

N ick let her lie in the next day, which was Sunday. The first thing she was aware of was the clink of a mug on the bedside table beside her.

"Rise and shine," he said, perching on the edge of the bed with a grin.

"What time is it?" She sat up.

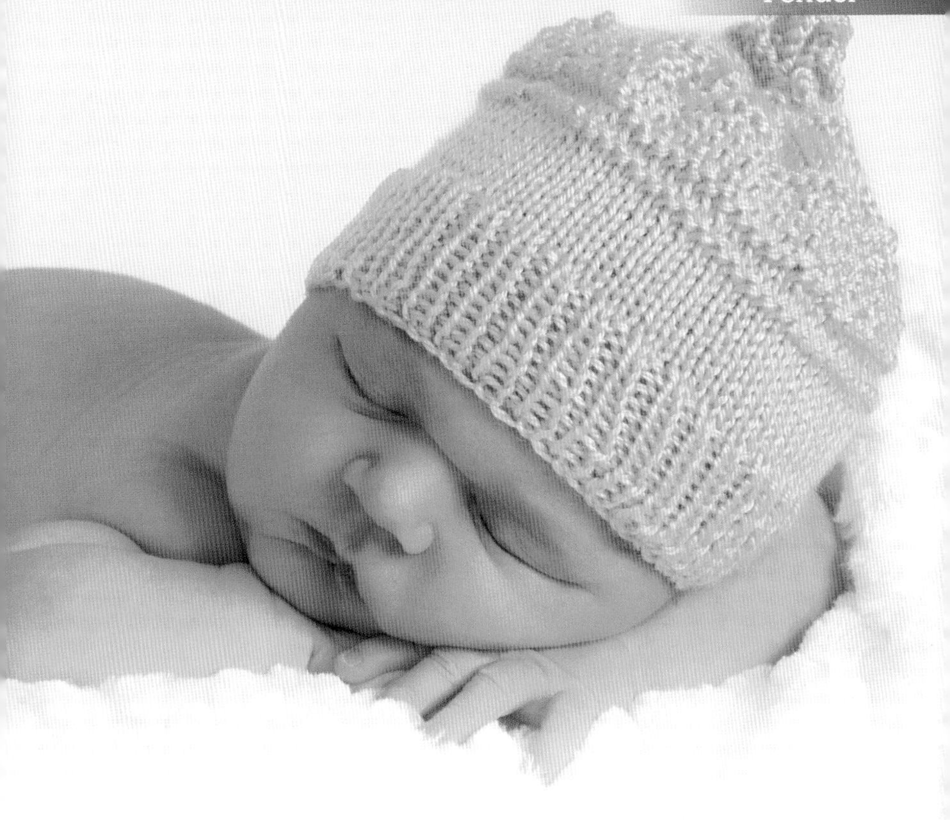

"Coming up for nine o'clock."

"Gosh, how lazy I am."

He leaned forward and kissed her on the forehead.

"Hardly lazy – you were up with Madam half the night. She's not tired. She's just had a hearty breakfast."

"I'll bet she has." It was then that Ellie noticed the tray that he'd put on his side of the bed. "I thought I could smell toast."

Not just toast, she saw, but butter in a little silver dish, a mini pot of Nutella and a single red rose in a stem vase.

"I'm married to an angel, aren't I?" she said with a grateful smile.

Nick gave his imaginary halo a quick polish. "I try!"

There had been a time when Ellie had thought she'd never be a mum. They'd had three miscarriages and two IVF attempts, and she'd been the grand old age of forty-two before she'd finally heard those magic words from her doctor.

"I think we're there, Ellie. I'm happy to confirm you're pregnant."

It had been worth the wait. *Oh so, so worth it,* she thought as she went downstairs to join Nick. As he had said, Millie was bright-eyed in her baby seat and she gurgled happily when Ellie came into the room so that her heart turned over with love, despite her tiredness.

At just after midday the doorbell rang.

Continued overleaf

ILLUSTRATIONS: ISTOCKPHOTO, REX/SHUTTERSTOCK

Continued from previous page

Ellie was giving Millie a feed in the conservatory so Nick went to answer it and she could hear familiar voices in the hall. Then, suddenly, the kitchen was full of people.

"Happy Mother's Day. You didn't think you were going to get away without going out for lunch, did you?"

"What? Now?" Ellie gasped, looking down at her tatty old baby-feeding blouse. "I'm not exactly dressed for it. You could have warned me, Nick."

"He was sworn to secrecy," Annabel told her with a giggle. She held out her arms. "I'll take Millie. You've got plenty of time to get ready."

So that's how they came to be sitting in Ocean Views that lunchtime, the five of them. Nick and herself, Annabel and James, and of course, Millie.

Millie was on her best behaviour, mostly because she was asleep in her buggy beside the table!

Ellie looked around at them all and her heart filled with warmth. To be out with her family on Mother's Day! This was as good as it got. For years she and Nick had avoided Mother's Day outings because seeing all those happy families had hurt too much.

Thank goodness Annabel and James hadn't had to wait so long. Millie had come along within months of them being married. She watched her daughter's face. The love in her eyes as she looked into the buggy – that expression Ellie knew so very well.

Annabel must have sensed her gaze because she glanced up. "Thank you so much for looking after her last night. We had a lovely time at the theatre. And it was a nice change, not having to get up in the night. I'd forgotten what sleep was like! She didn't get you up too often, did she?"

"She was as good as gold," Ellie said without a second's hesitation.

Because that's what you did when you were a mum, wasn't it? Told the occasional white lie and smiled while you did it. She reached across to touch her beloved daughter's hand.

"Happy Mother's Day, to you too, darling."

For years, seeing all those happy families had hurt too much

MY FAVOURITE...

My favourite book is *Jonathan Strange and Mr Norrell* by Susanna Clarke. The characters are so alive that I felt bereft when I finished. That's the mark of a great novel for me.

Brain BOOSTERS

Missing Link

The answer to each clue is a word which has a link with each of the three words listed. This word may come at the end (eg **HEAD** linked with **BEACH, BIG, HAMMER**), at the beginning (eg **BLACK** linked with **BEAUTY, BOARD** and **JACK**) or a mixture of the two (eg **STONE** linked with **HAIL, LIME** and **WALL**).

ACROSS

2 Crew, Cruiser, Log (5)
7 Back, Board, Chock (4)
8 Booby, Door, Fly (4)
9 Lamp, Light, Welding (3)
10 First, Sales, Spokes (6)
11 Lively, Over, Sharp (6)
13 Razor, Shoulder, Switch (5)
14 Back, Phone, Straight (6)
15 Cry, East, Reaching (3)
16 Bell, Chance, Clef (6)
18 Board, Cloth, Paper (5)
21 Eye, Power, Spanner (6)
23 Carriage, Day, Ticket (6)
25 Boiled, Radio, String (3)
26 Jugular, Thread, Varicose (4)
27 Chair, Listening, Stand (4)
28 Bareback, Bike, Out (5)

DOWN

1 Root, Stock, Sugar (4)
2 Book, Circuit, Doors (6)
3 Fire, Name, New (5)
4 Power, Reactor, Waste (7)
5 Foot, Music, Toad (6)
6 Brained, Jugged, March (4)
12 Hands, Linen, Tricks (5)
13 Back, Flea, Sound (5)
15 Bed, Duster, Weight (7)
17 Powder, Soda, Tray (6)
19 Earth, Land, Superior (6)
20 Forces, Fore, Robbery (5)
22 Fan, Glove, Ready (4)
24 Above, Pay, Sun (4)

Hidden word in the shaded squares:

Turn To Page 143 For Solutions

Shine A Light

You may wonder why some people come into your life,
but it might be that it just takes a little time…

By Barbara Dynes

DEVON, 1944

It felt funny, on that chilly April morning, to be going into school with Mum. We were late; Mum had gone on serving customers in our sweet shop right up to the last minute.

"Can't afford not to!" she'd declared.

I wrinkled my nose as we went into the big hall. School dinner smells of stale cabbage and lumpy custard hung in the air. But today there was no school.

"We've to pick an evacuee, Maggie," Mum had said. "Missed out earlier in the war and now we need to do our bit!"

"Doing our bit" was all very well, but would it mean sharing my dolls, clothes, rations and everything else?

"Ah, Mrs Owen, at last!" A WVS lady shouted across the hall. "There's not many left, I'm afraid."

I stared at the few children lined up under the window. Coats undone, socks around their ankles, gas masks trailing, some crying or sucking their thumbs.

"She'll do," Mum declared.

I blinked. Mum was pointing at a girl in a shabby green coat, standing alone,

staring sulkily at her feet. Every now and again she kicked out at the lad next to her.

"I like a bit of spirit," Mum added.

I frowned, wondering what "a bit of spirit" was and whether I had any.

The evacuee, called Pauline, was from London. She was ten, the lady said – only a couple of years older than me, yet she looked about twelve.

By the time the paperwork was done and I'd said hello to "the poor kid", as Mum kept calling her, I decided that "spirit" must mean trouble.

"I expect you're hungry, Pauline?" Mum beamed, as we walked back to the shop. "Will Marmite sandwiches do you?"

"Ugh!" Pauline made sick noises.

"Spam, then?" Mum suggested.

I felt cross. Why should she get a choice when I never did?

Later, with Mum busy in the shop, I had to show Pauline around. Seeing the Anderson shelter in the garden, she just sniggered.

"Bombs, 'ere in the sticks? Some 'ope!"

She shrugged off everything like that, not letting on much about herself – or at least, not until we were in our beds.

"Me dad's an invalid." Pauline's voice, with its funny accent, sounded crackly in the dark, like people on the wireless. "A bad back. Is your dad in the war?"

"He was. He was killed."

Funny, I could say it, yet I didn't really believe it. Wanting to cry, I was glad Mum's curtains did such a good blackout job. "We miss him."

There was a silence. Then she said, in a show-off voice, "My dad's the best! He calls me his princess."

"He sounds nice."

Now my voice was the crackly one.

There was no answer. Pauline must have fallen asleep.

The next day, Mum had explained about our sweet ration and Pauline pulled a face. She'd thought that, living in a sweet shop, you were bound to get more than your three ounces each week.

"All them jars, full of sweets!" she'd said to me later. "You could 'elp yourself!"

Pauline had some daft ideas. But, thankfully, she was not bothered about my dolls. All she wanted to do after school was go out on my bike. I didn't mind about the bike but I did mind that I still got boring jobs like counting coupons for the Ministry of Food. Pauline was let off.

"She can't count very well," was Mum's excuse. OK, she wasn't very good at sums, but it still wasn't fair.

The Saturday the money went missing, Pauline had been out cycling with Agnes Grant from school. I'd stayed in, reading.

Pauline and I were eating our tea when Mum burst in.

Continued overleaf

"Someone's nicked a five-pound note from the till!" she cried. "I only had one in there, so own up!"

I gulped. Pauline stared at Mum, her big brown eyes wide.

"I been out all day, Mrs Owen," she said. "Ain't been near the shop!"

Mum looked at me. "Maggie?"

"Of course not, Mum! I'd never pinch money from the shop, you know that."

"Then it's a bloomin' mystery!" Mum declared grimly.

It stayed a mystery for ages.

But I felt bad about it because, when Mum had closed the shop at dinner time to go to the butcher's, I'd gone to fetch my Enid Blyton from the shelter at the

Mum never mentioned it again, but a bit of a barrier went up between me and Pauline from then on. Chalk and cheese, Mum called us.

LONDON, 1954

I was not sorry to see Pauline go back to London in 1945, just before the end of the war.

Yet, years afterwards, some of the little things she did still rankled. Perhaps unfairly, I included the missing five-pound note among them. Silly, when Mum herself seemed to have forgotten about it.

Anyway, on business in London with my insurance firm, I found myself close to where Pauline lived. Call it sheer curiosity but, at a loose end one evening, I decided

"There's often a reason behind bad behaviour," Mum said. "So don't judge"

bottom of the garden. On the way back I got talking to Mr Stranks next door for a while. The back door was open all that time – maybe someone had sneaked in?

Then one day at school, Agnes told me that she and Pauline had come back to the shop that day. Pauline knew that Mum was going out at dinner time and thought I was going with her. So she had sneaked in, pinching a handful of pear drops and humbugs.

"Was that all?" I asked.

She nodded. I didn't mention the missing money then, but in bed that night I asked Pauline about it again.

"Yeah, I took a few sweets," she admitted. "But no money, though!"

I didn't believe her.

to take a bus there and look in on her.

A tall, gangly young man answered the door of the small terraced house. When I mentioned Pauline he shook his head.

I explained who I was.

"Ah, I'm her stepbrother, Robbie. Pauline left home years ago, I'm afraid." He smiled. "Why don't you come in?"

We sat in a small, but cosy living room. Photos of last year's Coronation lined the sideboard and, seeing my interest, he said he was a trainee news photographer.

Then he leaned forward and told me, "My dad married Pauline's mother, Eva, a few years back. Her father died just after the war ended."

"Oh, what a pity! I got the impression she thought a lot of him."

He shook his head. "You've got that wrong," he said. "He treated her really badly. I won't go into details…" Robbie hesitated. "That was why Eva wanted Pauline evacuated. Mind you, he was rough with Eva, too. She told me Pauline once sent her money from Devon – a gift from your mother. That was so kind!"

Robbie smiled at me warmly. But I couldn't answer; I was too busy thinking about Pauline. So our evacuee really was a "poor kid".

He went to make tea and when he came back I asked more about her.

"Our Pauline's a bit of a nomad. She rarely comes home, but I do try to watch out for her."

"And her mother?"

"She and my father emigrated to Australia after the wedding. A real happy-ever-after there."

Later, Robbie shook my hand, promising to keep in touch, but I didn't really expect him to. I was just glad that someone was looking out for Pauline, wherever she may be. The icy edge to our relationship had thawed a little.

Mum's reaction was typical. She said she'd half-guessed the truth at the time.

"There's often a reason behind bad behaviour, Maggie," she remarked. "Remember that, before condemning anyone in future."

DEVON, 2016

My eightieth birthday… I can hardly believe it! Both sons, grandchildren and all the family are all here to celebrate.

My husband, bless him, booked this local hall and organised all the arrangements… balloons everywhere, a disco and far too much food.

Sue, my friend, bangs on the table.

"A word about Maggie, our war baby," she declares. "Old enough to remember such things as gas masks, Spam, dripping, dried egg and moaning air raid sirens – whatever they are…"

I join in the laughter and glance across to where Pauline sits – a frail Pauline now, with bad arthritis. Yet the way she's scowling at her son shows she's not lost that "bit of spirit". We keep in touch, Pauline and I. The connection is still there, although we'll never be that close.

"Come on now, Mags!" Sue cries. I realise that my husband and I are expected to start the dancing.

I move into his arms, knowing I'm safe with him in more ways than one. He's a good dancer – he learned back, in the old days of the Hammersmith Palais and Joe Loss.

I smile up at him. I've never been happier. And in a roundabout way that's thanks to Pauline.

"I love you, Maggie," he murmurs.

"I love you, too, Robbie," I reply.

● ●

MY FAVOURITE…

My favourite memory is of my mother running a sweet shop during the war. Our friends were amazed that my sister and I were only allowed strict rations like everyone else – not one extra sweet!

Down By The River Wye

Who was coming into her life across the swift flowing river?

By Alison Carter

From the window of the room she was cleaning in the Old Ferrie Inn, Sally watched Hal Wyman pull the hand ferry across the Wye.

Even from up here, she could see the movement of his shoulder muscles and the tensing of his long legs. He flung his noose further along the overhead rope that spanned the river, dragged the punt across the water, and flung the noose again.

The passengers sat in the ferry, lifting their faces to the sun and looking up at the steep wooded banks. It was a pretty scene, not least because Hal was a fine thing to watch.

Sally knew, however, that he was a bad young man. He was a disappointment to the Wymans, a gambler by twenty and now, twenty-two and without a penny to his name, not to be trusted with the family business, the Saracen Inn.

"Sal, are you done?"

It was Lizzy Wyman outside the door.

Continued overleaf

Historical Romance

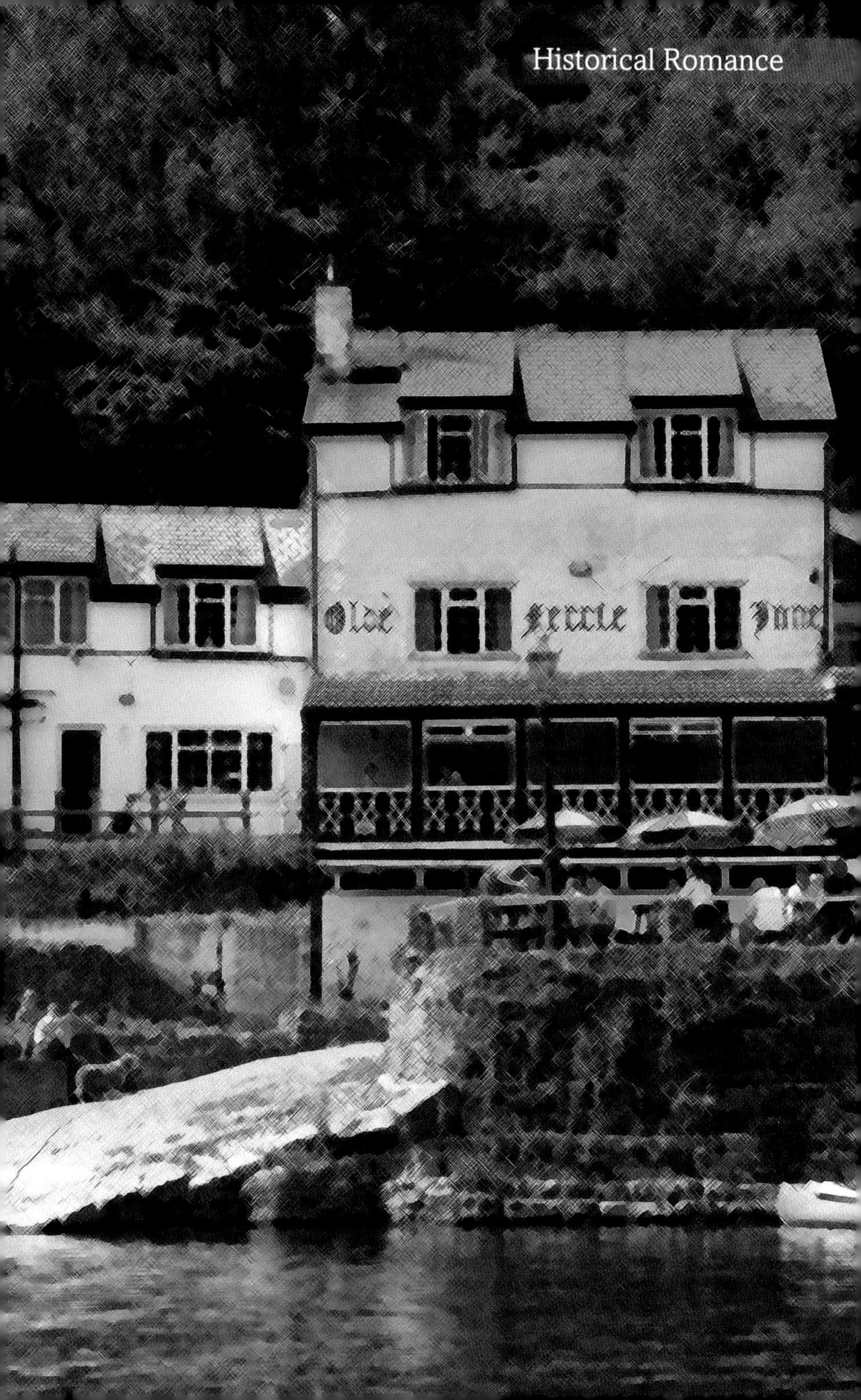

Continued from previous page

Lizzy was Hal's sister and the girls had been friends since childhood, though Sally was of humbler stock. She had come over on the hand ferry to fetch Sally for a walk.

"Just got to fetch a clean chamber pot!" Sal said as Lizzy pushed open the door.

Through the sunlit window, Lizzy noticed her brother. Her mouth tightened.

"No one really wanted Hal back home," she said. "My Aunt Betsy says he should have been sent away again for a wastrel."

"But he's observing your father's curfew, and isn't he taking that ferry across all day, every day?"

"All summer, Father insists, if he's to redeem himself. Hal says he'll work out his debt and earn his board. Yes, he's behaving. But that doesn't make my brother into a George Mills."

"No one is a George Mills." Sally smiled.

George was Lizzy's fiancé, a hard-working, outspoken, upright man much admired in Symonds Yat and beyond. He was in shipping, destined for great things.

Head on the east. They all liked Lizzy and wanted her Michaelmas marriage to be a grand celebration. People pitied the Wymans because their son had spent all his modest allowance and accumulated debts. The village, on both banks, was supporting Lizzy.

But all this planning brought Sally into contact often with Hal, and it made her uneasy. She could never think of him as a beau. It wasn't only that he was wicked, it was that the Wymans were so above her own family, who made charcoal in the Forest of Dean.

"Oh, there's George!" Lizzy exclaimed, "come to see me. I must get across to join him." She waved, but George, striding along the bank towards the Saracen's in his handsome silk hat, didn't notice.

Hal, however, looked up as he moored the punt by the Saracen's, and called across the river, "Sally Harris, how are you today?"

Lizzy stepped to the water's edge. "Pull across. George will want me," she called

Sally glanced at the distant figure of Hal, and wished he were a George, because she had such a fancy for him since he came home from Gloucester that it kept her awake at night. He'd gone to learn clerking, had left a boy and come back, well… a man. But a bad man.

The girls walked along the river and Lizzy talked about her wedding. Everyone at the Old Ferrie Inn on the west bank knew everyone at the Saracen's

Sally blushed. Hal stood with his forearm shading his eyes against the sun, and she thought she'd never seen anything so beautiful.

"He knows how to charm a woman," Lizzy said sharply. "Don't you go taking up with Hal. Girls should avoid my brother."

Lizzy stepped to the water's edge. "Pull across," she called. "George will want me."

As soon as they were across the river, Lizzy hurried into the inn.

"Wedding in five weeks," said Hal.

"It's going to be wonderful," Sally said.

"No doubt," said Hal dryly. He was

looking at the door of the inn. Sally reckoned he was jealous of George Mills.

"He's a fine man," she said, "a good man. He's going to be promoted at the shipyard in Chepstow – chief accountant, Lizzy says."

"I don't know if that makes you a good man," said Hal. He looked down at Sally, whose gaze was held by the dark hair falling over his brow. "But what do I know? You got a young man, Sally Harris?"

"Of course not!" Sally said, and realised how odd she sounded. "You'll need to catch that rope."

The ferry's mooring rope lay untethered. But he didn't move from his spot close beside her.

Then he sighed. "If you had a sister, Sally, and that sister needed maybe to know a thing, and you weren't sure if…" Hal stopped, and looked at Sal. "Never mind. It's not for me to rock boats. Speaking of which…"

He bent and yanked violently on the rope, as though in anger. Water splashed up the bank and Sal stepped back.

"Don't!"

He grinned. "I never do the right thing, do I?" he said. "I'm wicked Hal."

"They say you're mending your ways," Sal said. He was talking in riddles.

Then George came out of the inn, by the side door, and noticed them.

"Wyman, I couldn't find your father," he said in his booming voice, "and I haven't time to chat to barmaids."

"Indeed," said Hal in a dull voice, and George looked at him with narrow eyes.

"You're an impudent dog, for a man who doesn't deserve to be," George said.

Sally dropped a curtsey.

"Mr Mills, you must have missed Lizzy. She went inside only minutes ago."

"Did she?" George said. "I'm afraid I have to go. Send Lizzy my best." He smiled. "Send her a fiancé's love, and…" he looked about him, and finally down at his tailcoat. "And this."

He took a rosebud from his buttonhole and handed it to Sally. She stared at it and wondered how it must be to have a lover like George Mills.

Sally loved helping Lizzy arrange the wedding breakfast. But she saw how Hal increasingly began to irritate all the Wymans. He worked, but he was what Mrs Wyman called "slippery" about his sister's important day. He avoided talking about his part in it.

"I think George's superiority makes him tetchy," Mr Wyman said. Sally had been called to do some extra dusting work for Mrs Wyman, who was anxious to get the inn spick and span. "He's doing his best, but he's conscious that George has done so well and is only a few years older."

"Hal will come right," said Mrs Wyman, who adored her son.

"Will I now?" Hal has come in from the river, the hems of his breeches damp.

"Oh, here you are, Hal," Mrs Wyman said happily. "Go up and see Lizzy. She has stockings for you from Hereford and wants to know if you favour the colour."

"I don't care about stockings," Hal said sullenly. "This damned wedding."

Continued overleaf

"Don't curse, my boy. It will break your sister's heart if you go on like this."

Hal slumped onto a stool. He put his head in his hands, and his mother reached over and ruffled his thick hair. Sal tried not to look at him too long.

"I must not make Lizzy unhappy," he said automatically.

"There are many things you must do, son," said Mrs Wyman. "Just now, you must take yourself off the rug, because you are dripping river water. Be thoughtful, prove yourself mended."

"Perhaps I'll never mend," Hal said. "Perhaps it's not just I who need mending." He stood and crossed to the stairwell. Sally was there pulling cobwebs with a duster, and he saw her and smiled.

"Perhaps not everyone," he said, and looked for a moment into her eyes.

Lizzy complained that she didn't see enough of her lover. "He is always in Chepstow or Hereford," she said.

Yet Sally knew Lizzy was proud of George. She liked that he was busy, because it showed she was marrying a successful man.

"George says being married cannot stop him travelling," Lizzy said. "The shipping business never stands still, he says."

Sally wanted a husband. Lizzy told her she was pretty, and that she might find a man like George with good luck. Men with great prospects married maids, on occasion.

Still, Sally began to think she didn't really want a George Mills. It began to dawn on her, on the few occasions when she saw him, that he made her yawn. Sally wanted a husband who could make her laugh, a man who'd climb Symonds Yat Rock of an evening, hot and happy, pull her up beside him with a strong arm and look at the grand views with her. She hoped for a husband who had more to talk about by her fireside than commercial cargoes.

One morning early, Sally came out of the Saracen's Head with a broom and saw George and Hal talking near the inn. Out of some instinct, she stayed out of sight in the lee of the wall.

"You know no such thing, Wyman!" Mills' voice was a low growl. "And even supposing you did, which of us would be believed, d'you think?"

"You're a…" Hal's jaw was set hard, his fist clenched. "I've no words for you. You had better keep your promises, at least where my sister is concerned."

George smiled. "I adore Elizabeth," he said. "A fellow can love his wife and be… occupied elsewhere too."

The two men faced each other for a long moment, until George turned away.

Sally re-ran their conversation in her mind. Had Hal been telling George how much he disliked him, and accusing George of neglecting his sister for his business? Their mutual mistrust was well known. But Hal couldn't afford to have George Mills give bad reports of him, and so it must remain a private little feud, Sally knew.

It was only a week before Lizzy's wedding when Sally went out late one evening to beat rugs. The weather was strange, with a yellow light, hot still air and low black clouds gathering. Sally wondered if there'd be a late summer storm. She heard the inn door slam hard, and the figure of Hal Wyman appeared at the corner of the building. He was tense, bouncing on his soles, shoulders hunched.

"Hal?" Sally flung the rug over the clothes line. He swung round, and she saw that his eyes blazed.

"He's in Ross now, a-betraying of my sister!" he said in a constricted voice.

"What?" Sally came nearer. Hal exhaled.

"I wanted to keep it from you of all people, Sally. But it's bursting inside me.

throwing a party for her birthday – a private affair. A party! Before he takes Lizzy down the aisle! At least then I'd be sure, and I might tell Lizzy, though she'd not listen. She'd say I spoke out of spite –"

"I will be witness," Sally interrupted.

It was as though the world had shifted in its axis and everything was changed. He gazed at her, and seemed to wake from a dream.

"We can take the ferry, use a horse –"

"You've no horse."

"I'll take a horse."

"Steal, Hal, and you trying to be forgiven? And remember your curfew? It's nearly dark."

"But you'll come with me?"

Rain poured down her dress in rivulets, and lightning flashed across the sky.

She nodded, and he reached across the

He stared at her as a sheet of rain fell out of the sky on them and thunder rolled

Forgive me! A man in the snug, just come from Ross-on-Wye this evening with an urgent load – he says Mills is with his woman there now." He looked at Sally, his face pleading. "A wife, Sally, kept hidden so he can have Lizzy and her money!"

"But nobody listens to me, to wicked Hal. Mills knows it, and he keeps his secret using money and influence. Nobody there dare tell it."

"What will you do?"

He stared at her as a sheet of rain fell out of the sky on them, and a great clap of thunder rolled around the woodland.

"Do? I want to go to Ross, and see, to catch him at the inn where they say he keeps her. My friend in there says he's

space between them, pulled her to him and kissed her.

"The river's getting up," he said, and Sally looked at the white water and the waves surging against the banks.

"The hand ferry's too fragile for this weather," she said.

"I'll get us across," he said, and then he kissed her again.

They ran, dragged down by water and confused by lightning flashes, to the ferry point opposite the Saracen's Head. The punt dipped and reared as he handed Sally down into it.

She clutched on to the sides, and
Continued overleaf

Continued from previous page

Hal flung the noose with all his might, and it was clear he aimed to cross the river in as few hauls as was humanly possible.

"If we're not quick, that man will slip away again, or he'll hear of my coming," Hal said. He called his words over the waves and the thunder. The storm was overhead, and fierce.

Sally watched his hand grow white as he held the noose tightly. The ferry had no safety rope: if he lost his grip on it, yanked from side to side as he was by the waves, they'd be tossed along the river to the weirs.

Sally couldn't swim, and in this weather swimming was no use anyway. The Wye could be a hungry river in a storm. All the muscles of Hal's body strained, and Sally's heart stopped each time the noose was thrown loose from the soaking guide rope. But he looked back at her and grinned, and she felt, as water chilled every inch of her and she began to shake, that she was queen of the world.

Hal took his father's best horse from the Saracen's stable, and they rode faster than Sally had ever moved in her life. She held on round his waist, and as they rode, and the rain plastered her hair to her back, she told him she loved him.

"And I you," he called back to her. "I got back from Gloucester to find my sister's playmate a beauty!"

In an inn on the edge of the town they pushed their way through a rowdy gathering towards a low door. Hal shoved aside a man who seemed to stand guard, and threw open the door.

Mills sat in a carver chair, a tankard in his hand and a laughing woman in his lap. At first he bluffed; Hal had no witness.

"My friends won't disturb my happiness," he said, looking about him, smiling complacently. "I've loyal friends."

"I can bear witness," Sally said, stepping from the shadows. George Mills fell silent.

Hal snaked an arm around her waist, and she felt the tension in his body subside.

"You're so cold, Sally," he said softly. "What have I done to you?"

She laughed, and everyone stared.

"I'm cold and I'm wet, and I'm the happiest woman alive!"

Lizzy hadn't long to wait before she found a better man. She was a bright and pretty girl who had learned better how to choose.

Sally married Hal Wyman that Christmastime, and Mr Wyman made him partner in the inn and the family farm. They hired another young man to pull the hand ferry, and sometimes Hal would ask his wife if she liked to watch the young man from a window.

Sally would laugh, and kiss him, and say she had enough to do – what with the inn, and the children, and a husband to amuse – without standing to watch the ferryman go by.

● ●

MY FAVOURITE...

My favourite place is the Wye Valley. It's so atmospheric! Rowing past the ancient pubs on calm waters last summer, this story came to me instantly.

Brain BOOSTERS

Missing Link

The answer to each clue is a word which has a link with each of the three words listed. This word may come at the end (eg **HEAD** linked with **BEACH, BIG, HAMMER**), at the beginning (eg **BLACK** linked with **BEAUTY, BOARD** and **JACK**) or a mixture of the two (eg **STONE** linked with **HAIL, LIME** and **WALL**).

Turn To Page 143 For Solutions

ACROSS

1 Crier, Home, Tinsel (4)
3 Colour, Feather, School (7)
9 Fitted, Garden, Sink (7)
10 Market, Shower, Side (5)
11 Candle, Nose, Numeral (5)
13 Bin, Bridge, Full (5)
14 Human, Thought, Words (4)
16 Film, Special, Time (5)
18 Money, Oxford, Tea (4)
19 Back, Pushers, Soft (5)
21 Cough, Golden, Maple (5)
23 Back, Hold, Lend (5)
24 Heat, Ill, Well (7)
25 High, Relative, Vapour (7)
26 Doe, Eagle, Starry (4)

DOWN

1 Care, Risk, Under (6)
2 Can, Hole, Mouth (8)
4 Also, Around, Sack (3)
5 Free, Perry, Stone (5)
6 Ale, Time, World (4)
7 Hand, Over, Sheet (6)
8 Flash, Gates, Plain (5)
12 Cycle, Launch, Outboard (5)
15 Cottage, Heavy, Service (8)
17 Baked, Cooking, Crab (6)
18 Beef, Boy, Off (5)
20 Crash, Gentry, Interest (6)
21 Cow, Potting, Tool (5)
22 Blind, Line, Palm (4)
24 Bit, Great, Tom (3)

Hidden word in the shaded squares:

The Amethyst
Brooch

It could have made us enemies forever… but instead something wonderful happened

By Sue Johnston

I stood outside the charity shop gazing through the window at the amethyst brooch on the black velvet display board. It was gold and oval shaped, the colours of the stones fading from deep purple to almost white. The brooch glittered and flashed rainbows of light.

I stood there on the frosty pavement as time spun backwards by fifty years. I hardly noticed the cold, remembering what it was like to be ten years old and in a complete fever of excitement about Christmas coming.

I particularly remembered how I felt when our teacher, Miss Furze, handed out letters about the fancy dress competition to be held during the end of term party.

"The whole point of the exercise, children, is that these costumes are to be YOUR OWN WORK."

Miss Furze always talked in capital letters when she wanted to make an important point. Her hair was like grey candyfloss and she had steel-blue eyes behind round glasses.

"I know most of your mothers are very clever, but I'd like to test *your* ingenuity."

Sounds a bit girly to me, Jane," said my friend Sam as we walked home. He kicked a stone into the gutter where it collided with a tin can with a satisfying clang. His shoe-laces were undone and his shirt was streaked with ink. He liked to think he was big and tough and never bothered to wear a jacket, even when it was raining.

"Might be fun," I said cautiously.

"Shouldn't think so," he said moodily, stuffing his fists into his trouser pockets.

I hoped his bad mood wouldn't last too long. I liked playing out with Sam. We did fun things like climbing trees and making dens. I felt really pleased when he said gruffly that I wasn't bad "for a girl".

It wasn't that I didn't like doing girl things – I did. I just didn't have a particular friend to do them with. We'd moved to Oldsworthy six months ago and I'd had to change schools. It was the last year of primary school and all the girls seemed to have paired off with a best friend – except me.

The only person in the class who was newer than me was a girl called Susan Clarke. Her family had moved into a house near the park a few weeks ago.

So far she'd come top in every test we'd had – which had put a few people's noses out of joint.

I'd tried to talk to her – Miss Furze said we had to make her feel welcome.

"Perhaps you could invite her for tea," suggested Mum.

"She won't come," I said. "She spends every break time in the library reading or walking round the playground on her own."

"She could be shy," said Mum.

I didn't think so. I thought she was stuck-up because she lived in a posher area than most of us.

"I bet she wins the fancy dress competition," said Sam as Susan walked past us, careful not to splash her ultra-white socks in the puddles. "She'll probably go to that shop in town and buy a really cool outfit."

"Weren't you listening? It's not about buying something to wear. We've got to use our imaginations and see what there is lying around at home that we can make into a costume."

"Well, I still think she'll win it," said Sam, indicating Susan's retreating back with a jerk of his head. "She's come first in every single thing else since she came to the school."

"I bet she can't climb trees as well as you can," I said brightly, trying to make him feel better.

"She'd probably find a way," he said, pushing open his front gate.

Continued overleaf

That evening, I sat at the kitchen table trying to think of something original to wear. There was never much room in our kitchen as my mum took in washing. I was sandwiched between a clothes-horse festooned with damp sheets on one side and the ironing board on the other.

"You'll worry a hole in that tablecloth staring at it like that, Jane," said Mum. "Have a look at one of your story books. That might give you an idea."

I looked through several books before I decided what to do.

pinned on it. She looked very strict.

"It's a shame for Susan," said my mum. "No brothers or sisters to play with."

Sometimes I envied her. With an older sister and two younger brothers, it was sometimes difficult to get much privacy in our house – particularly as my sister, Cathy, and I shared a room.

Cathy was sixteen and had just started work in an office. Her side of the room was full of things like hair dryers and lipsticks, pop records and fashion magazines. The room smelled of hair spray and nail varnish.

"Told you she'd win. The rest of us might as well not have bothered..."

Everyone at school was excited about the competition. There were lots of whispered hints and nudges, but Miss Furze had told us to keep our ideas a secret until the day.

"It will be more of a surprise when you see what everyone else has created," she declared.

Susan Clarke didn't say anything but she looked very smug. My mum said that Susan had once lived in a big house. Then her dad had lost money on something called the stock market and they'd had to move to somewhere smaller.

Susan wore shop-bought cardigans instead of hand-knitted ones like the rest of us, and she spent ages practising her spellings at break time when the rest of us were out playing.

"Mummy will be cross with me if I don't get them right," she said.

Susan's mother wore a coat with a fur collar and a hat with a glittery brooch

She could sometimes be a bit moody – Mum said it was her age – but when I told her about my fancy dress costume she offered to lend me her black skirt.

"Just mind you don't tear it or drop jelly down it," she said.

She was taller than me so the skirt reached nearly to my ankles. I planned to wear my black school swimming costume underneath it.

"You'll need something to cover your arms – it'll be cold," said my gran when I went to see her after school one day. "I'll lend you my shawl if you give me a share of your winnings."

The shawl was triangular, made of soft black wool and had tassels round the edge. Mum loaned me a silver pin to fasten it with.

It took me several evenings to make a witch's hat out of a big piece of corrugated paper that I'd painted black. The paper was stiff to cut and my round-ended scissors were blunt. Mum wouldn't let me use her dress-making scissors.

"They are not to be used for cutting paper," she said.

My hands were sore by the time I'd finished.

"I wish I could've helped you, Jane," said Mum, but you know what that letter said. "It has to be your own work."

On the day of the party, I borrowed Dad's birch besom from the garden and my younger brother's toy cat. The cat was ginger and white which wasn't quite the right colour for a witch, but it was the best I could do.

Mum walked to school with me to make sure I didn't trip over the birch besom or the hem of Cathy's skirt. Besides, I think she was as curious as I was to see what everyone else had created.

The first person I saw when I arrived in the playground was Susan Clarke.

She was resplendent in a sugar pink silk Cinderella-at-the-ball creation with glittery silver shoes and crystal tiara. It was clearly not "all her own work" and it must have cost a fortune.

I felt sick with disappointment as I joined the circle of fairies, nurses and pirates, knowing that Susan was bound to win the prize.

"I told you she'd win it. The rest of us might as well not have bothered," said Sam. Despite his comments about this being girly, he'd obviously put a lot of effort into his costume. He was dressed as a pirate in his brother's stripy T-shirt and leather belt, a silver-painted cardboard dagger with a smattering of red paint for blood on it and a black patch over one eye.

"Miss Furze has probably forgotten what she said by now," said another girl, dressed as a fairy with trailing wings made from an old net curtain and a home-made tiara covered in glitter. "Susan's bound to win."

We walked round the hall three times. Long tables had been set out on one side of the hall with party food on them – sausage rolls, crisps and iced cakes.

Miss Furze and two other teachers watched us closely. We stood, feeling awkward, in little groups while the teachers made up their minds. It took ages.

"It was a hard decision," said Miss Furze eventually, "but the winner is…"

Susan Clarke took a step forward, a beaming smile on her face.

"The winner is Jane Thomas," said Miss Furze.

Susan stepped back, her face crumpled with disappointment.

"You've won, Jane," said Sam excitedly, pushing me forward.

I stepped forward on shaking legs and took the small box that Miss Furze offered me, somehow remembering to shake hands with her.

"Well done," she said. "I can tell you've put in a lot of time and effort."

Sam got second prize and one of the fairies was third.

I lifted the lid from the box and gazed

Continued overleaf

Continued from previous page

in wonder at the brooch nestled on the plump cushion of white satin inside. I'd never seen anything so pretty. I'd never been given a piece of jewellery before. The brooch was beautiful and the purple stones shimmered when the light caught them.

"It's an odd prize to give a child," said one of the mums helping to lay out the sausage rolls and sandwiches. "Just as well it wasn't a boy who won."

I thought it was a magical prize. I held it tightly in my hand and kept looking at it.

I was surprised to see Susan in tears,

"That's not yours, Susan Clarke. Give it back to Jane immediately and tell her you're sorry."

I never found out what happened next because mothers started arriving to collect their children. I was so excited showing Mum, Cathy and Gran my new brooch that I forgot all about Susan until the next morning.

I was surprised that she wasn't at school – especially as it was the last day of term and we were going to have games.

After she'd done the register, Miss Furze asked me to take it to the secretary's office. I was just in time to see

"She doesn't need to be so anxious. She should concentrate on making friends"

being comforted by Miss Furze.

"Mummy's going to be so cross," Susan was saying between sobs. "That dress cost a lot of money."

"That's the point, dear, it wasn't supposed to cost anything except time," said Miss Furze.

There were two of us who didn't eat much tea that day – Susan because she was so upset and me because although I was excited about winning, I felt so sorry for Susan. I could see how worried she was about telling her mother that she hadn't won.

I knew it wasn't the brooch that Susan really wanted – it was being able to tell her mum that she'd come first. I didn't see her take it, but one minute it was there beside my plate and the next minute it had gone.

Miss Furze had spotted her though.

Susan and her mum going into the head teacher's office. They both looked as if they'd been crying.

The secretary asked me to wait while she found a letter that needed to go back to Miss Furze. She scurried away, her feet in their brown lace-up shoes tap-tapping on the stone floor of the corridor, leaving me alone in the office.

I didn't mean to eavesdrop but I couldn't help overhearing what the head teacher was saying.

"Susan is doing very well, Mrs Clarke. There are no problems with her school work so she doesn't need to be so anxious. She should concentrate on making friends."

"It's been a very difficult time for all of us," said Mrs Clarke. She sounded tearful. "We've all had to make a lot of changes due to financial setbacks. It hasn't been easy for Susan – she's a bit shy and doesn't find it easy to make friends."

The secretary came back at that point and told me to hurry back to Miss Furze with the letter. As I went along the corridor, I had an idea. There was something I could do to help Susan after all – I could be her friend.

I invited her round for tea during the Christmas holidays and it became the start of a long friendship. We came from very different homes but she loved the hustle and bustle of mine – playing Ludo or Snakes and Ladders with me and my brothers or helping my mum make cakes.

I used to go to her house. I was a bit nervous at first because the place was full of antique furniture and I was worried about scratching or scuffing something.

Susan's mum was very kind once you got to know her. She was very good at needlework and taught me to use her sewing machine. She often said if her husband hadn't lost his money, she'd never have had the courage to start her dressmaking business.

Sam let Susan come tree climbing with us. He was a bit grudging at first.

"If she turns out to be a cry-baby then she can't come again."

Susan turned out to be really good.

"Not bad for a girl," was the highest praise from Sam.

Once our teenage years were over I wasn't surprised when they started dating, although they kept it a secret at first – even from me.

Susan and I were friends all through our senior school years and even went to the same secretarial college. We exchanged confidences and I was the first person she told when Sam asked her to be his wife. Their wedding was simple but beautiful. I was their only bridesmaid in pale blue satin.

A year later their first daughter was born and they named her Jane after me.

I'm suddenly aware of how cold my feet are. I don't know how long I've been gazing at the brooch on its black velvet background, travelling back into the past.

All I know is that tomorrow is the fiftieth anniversary of that fancy dress competition. Susan and I are meeting for lunch and I think of how special our friendship has been, and how it may not have happened without the competition.

I push open the door, unpin the brooch from the board and take it to the counter.

"That's very pretty," said the assistant as she wrapped the brooch in tissue paper and placed it in a small black box.

"It's for my best friend," I said.

MY FAVOURITE...

The Far Pavilions by M M Kaye is a brilliant novel set in 19th-century India vibrating with great characters, atmospheric settings, gripping action and a happy ending.

Garden Of Eden

Some things are not what they seem – and what's right
for you could be right there in front of you all along

By Glenda Young

He looks shorter than he does on the telly," Mandy said, peering to get a better view.

"I think he looks younger in real life, too," Sue remarked.

"But he's every bit as gorgeous as we expected him to be," declared Mandy, who was now scrabbling in her handbag to find her phone so that she could take a photograph.

"He's wearing his silk scarf too, Mandy! Oh look, it really suits him."

Claire sighed and gripped the plant pot she was holding on her knee.

When she'd heard that the famous TV gardener Danny Bloom was coming to their local garden centre to give a talk, she knew she couldn't miss it. Danny Bloom was her favourite. He was knowledgeable about his subject, he was engaging and funny, and yes, it just so happened that he was a very attractive man too. His thick dark hair, winning smile that showed off his dimples to perfection, and his lean frame was a killer combination that had proved a ratings winner.

However, when Claire had asked her friends Mandy and Sue if they'd like to accompany her to Danny Bloom's talk, she hadn't expected them to dissolve into giggles like a couple of schoolgirls!

"His wife's a very lucky lady," Mandy enthused, holding her phone high above the heads of the people in the row in front of them.

"Madam! Please!" a stern voice said from behind. "Some of us are trying to concentrate on Mr Bloom's talk. Would you mind putting your phone down so that we can actually see him?"

Mandy dropped her hand and sheepishly put away her camera before turning to the man in the row behind, whispering her apologies. She and Sue exchanged a smile.

"Hey, I've taken loads of photos of him," Mandy said.

"Let's have a look!" Sue replied.

The friends were engrossed looking at Mandy's phone for the next few minutes while in front of them on the stage, in person, Danny Bloom was engaging with his audience of amateur gardeners.

Claire didn't blame Mandy and Sue too much for going gooey-eyed at Danny Bloom, he really was one of the most

handsome men on television. But she also knew that Mandy and Sue didn't know the first thing about gardening and had no interest in it. Claire, on the other hand, was a dab hand with her borders and managed her small back garden with pride.

For as long as she could remember, Claire had tuned in every Saturday morning to watch *Blooming Lovely*, the gardening show hosted by Danny. It was broadcast from his own garden in the Midlands, a three-acre site called March Gardens, complete with long borders, two ponds, three greenhouses, a rockery, rose garden, vegetable patch and orchard.

Each time the programme aired, Danny's pet dog, a Dalmatian called Spot, followed him around March Gardens, posing for the camera or lying at his feet as Danny addressed the camera.

Through watching *Blooming Lovely*, Claire knew that as well as his dog and his trademark red silk scarf, Danny Bloom was married – and happily too. He often referred to his wife as "the lovely Suzanne", although she was too shy to be seen on screen.

When Danny Bloom's talk ended, Claire balanced the plant pot on her knees as she joined in with the enthusiastic applause.

"Now," Danny said, peering out into the audience with the cheeky smile that had won so many admirers. "Did anyone take up the challenge to bring an unusual plant in for me?"

Continued overleaf

Claire clasped her plant pot with her left hand and her right shot up in the air.

"Yes?" Danny said from the stage, pointing in the direction of Claire. "The lady in the red jacket at the back?"

Claire stood and felt herself blushing as heads in the room turned towards her.

"I've brought this…" she said, holding the small plant pot high.

From the stage, Danny Bloom peered out into the audience to see what was in Claire's hand, but she was too far away for him to see what it was.

One of the garden centre assistants approached Claire to ask if she could take the plant to Danny on the stage and Claire happily let the plant go.

On stage, Danny Bloom held Claire's plant pot to his face. He turned it around in his hand. He touched one of the tiny, delicate, orange leaves of the small plant Claire had brought along.

There was a hush in the audience as they awaited his verdict, but it took a long time to come – and when it did, it wasn't what they expected at all.

Danny looked out to the audience and fixed his attention on Claire at the back of the garden centre.

"Do you know…" he said finally. "In all my years doing these *Blooming Lovely* roadshows, I've never been stumped by an unusual plant. Never! But today… my word… I think it's happened for the very first time."

The audience broke into laughter and then, with a word in the ear of the garden centre assistant, Danny handed the plant pot back and it was soon returned to Claire's hands.

"Mr Bloom asks if he can chat to you for a few minutes before he leaves," the assistant said to Claire when she passed over the plant pot.

Mandy nudged Claire in the ribs. "Can we meet him too?" she pleaded.

"Say yes, Claire! Please let us meet him, too," Sue chimed in.

"Mr Bloom doesn't have much time to meet fans privately today, I'm afraid," the assistant said politely, addressing Claire. "But he would like to briefly meet *you* – to discuss the plant – before he leaves."

Mandy and Sue sulked off to the coffee shop, leaving Claire alone with her plant pot, waiting to meet Danny Bloom.

As he walked towards Claire, his silk scarf flapping open and his hair bouncing, she smiled and held out her hand in greeting.

"Nice to meet you," said Danny Bloom, shaking Claire's hand.

"I'm Claire," she replied.

"I know a few people who'd be very interested to see that plant," said Danny. "If it's as rare as I think it could be, we might need to get it into one of the laboratories – with your permission, of course – and carry out some research."

"I'd be delighted," smiled Claire, handing over the plant pot. "I don't much care for the plant anyway so I won't really miss it. It was something that grew from a packet of poppy seeds a couple of years ago. It must have made its way into the packet by mistake."

"So you're a lady who grows her own flowers from seeds?" Danny Bloom smiled at Claire and she felt herself blush.

"Look," he said. "If I take your plant in for research, how would you like to come down to March Gardens next week and I'll give you a tour before I hand the plant back?"

Claire's hand fluttered to her chest in sheer surprise.

"A tour of March Gardens? Of *your* gardens?" she gasped.

"The very same, as seen on TV,"

"But that's not right…" Claire gasped. "That's dishonest."

"It's television," Danny said, raising his eyebrows as if he too didn't fully approve. "But my two terriers Sparkler and Rocket never sit still, so they'd be no good on screen, always yapping and chasing each other everywhere."

"Oh…" Claire said, suddenly remembering her manners. "I've brought some flowers for your wife." She offered her small bouquet to Danny. "I cut them fresh from my garden this morning. I do hope she'll like them."

Danny Bloom ran his hand through his hair, apparently nonplussed.

"Ah, yes… my wife…" he said,

"I brought some flowers for your wife," Claire said. "Cut fresh from my garden"

Danny smiled. "Mind you, don't believe everything you see on TV – it's all smoke and mirrors really."

"Oh, I'd love to," Claire said. "Thank you. Thank you very much indeed."

I hope you don't mind if my dogs join us on our tour this morning?" Danny asked when Claire arrived at March Gardens the following week.

"You have more than one dog?" Claire asked, surprised. "I've only ever seen one of them on TV."

"You mean Spot the Dalmatian, right?" Danny laughed. "I'll let you into a little secret… Spot isn't mine. He belongs to my director but he looks so great on camera and the viewers love him, so we just pretend that Spot's mine, for the sake of the programme."

distractedly. "The lovely Suzanne, right?"

"Is she home today?" asked Claire. "It would be so good to meet her. I've never seen her in *Blooming Lovely*."

Danny sank onto one of his kitchen chairs and indicated with a hand for Claire to take a seat too.

"You've never seen her on TV, Claire, because she doesn't exist."

Claire sat back in her chair in shock.

"The TV company like to present me as a family man and so they not only gave me a dog that's not mine, but a wife I don't have, too."

Danny looked deep into Claire's eyes.

"I don't have a Dalmatian and I don't have a wife," he said. "I live in this big old crumbling pile with two acres of garden to manage and two crazy dogs to look after."

Continued overleaf

Continued from previous page

"You'll be telling me next your name's not really Danny Bloom," Claire laughed, a little too brightly, wondering how many more of his confessions she could take in.

Danny shook his head.

"No!" Claire cried. "Really?"

"Well, the only person who ever called me Danny was my mum. I'm Dan to anyone who knows me. But they changed my surname, for the programme. I'm really Daniel Bloemenfeld."

Claire let out a long, heavy sigh.

"I don't know what to make of all this," she said. "Is there anything at all about you that's real?"

Danny gazed almost longingly out of his kitchen window.

"Out there, that's real," he said, a wistful smile spreading across his face. "The trees and the flowers, the shrubs and the birds, the soil, the seeds… that's all very real."

Danny turned to Claire again and she could see his eyes sparkling as he talked about March Gardens.

"What's real are the flowers, the peppery aroma of lavender in the sunshine, the sherbet sweet scent of the rose bushes my mother planted years ago. What's real is the robin who visits every morning and sits on the windowsill, knocking at my window with his beak until I throw him some seed.

"March Gardens has been a part of me since before I can remember, Claire. And so I let *Blooming Lovely* present me any way they wish. If they want me to flirt with my fans down the camera lens, I'll do it. I'll flick my hair and undo the zip on my jacket. I'll do anything for the camera, for the programme… so long as it means I get to keep my family home and carry on with my work at the plant research lab."

There was a deep silence between them for a few moments as Claire took in all that he'd told her.

"And my plant?" she said finally. "Is there any news from your research lab about my plant?"

Danny nodded. "It's an extraordinary find," he said excitedly. "Let me tell you all about it on our tour around the gardens. There's just one thing though…"

"Yes?" asked Claire.

"The lab needs to keep your plant a while longer, you see. I could…" Danny paused. "I could bring it back to you, once the cuttings we've taken take root," he said. "That is… if you'd like me to?"

Claire smiled. She had a feeling she would need to keep Danny's visit a secret from Mandy and Sue.

"Well, Mr Bloemenfeld, if you can spare as much as two minutes, I could take you on a tour around my back garden when you visit?"

Danny smiled.

"In that case, I'll look forward to it," he said. "But please, call me Dan."

• •

MY FAVOURITE…

I love teenage and children's fiction, and one of my favourites is *The Mennyms* by Sylvia Waugh, a fabulous tale of living rag dolls.
Karen Byrom, Fiction Editor

Glazed Sausage Puffs

Ingredients
(Serves 8; 3 each)

- ◆ **500g pack puff pastry, thawed if frozen**
- ◆ **1 egg**
- ◆ **1tbsp wholegrain or Dijon mustard**
- ◆ **24 cocktail sausages**
- ◆ **2tbsp sweet chilli sauce, plus extra to serve**
- ◆ **2tsp honey**

1 Preheat the oven to 200°C, Fan oven 180°C, Gas Mark 6.

2 Roll out the pastry until it measures a little more than 20 x 30cm. Trim the edges with a sharp knife, then cut into 24 squares. Be sure to cut the edges cleanly, so that the pastry will rise well. Arrange on 2 greased baking sheets.

3 Beat the egg and mustard together, and brush evenly over the surface of the pastry. Place a cocktail sausage on top of each square, then bake for 20-22min.

4 Mix the sweet chilli sauce and honey together. Brush over the hot sausages, and return to the oven for a further 2-3min. Serve while warm, with extra sweet chilli sauce.

RECIPE AND FOOD STYLING: SUE ASHWORTH PHOTOGRAPHY JONATHAN SHORT

Jeremiah's Ghost

Clare discovered that the old smuggler's ghost wasn't as scary as all the locals seemed to think…

By Susan Sarapuk

"Smugglers used to operate along this beach," the woman in the shop had said. "There are all sorts of stories and legends about the history of this area the area."

Clare could well imagine it on a grey blustery winter's day…

High cliffs glowered over a deserted beach and the tide slowly crept in along the shore. She felt exposed as she walked along and almost fancied she could hear voices from the past carrying on the wind.

She pulled up her hood against the light squall and tucked her hands into the pockets of her raincoat.

In the height of summer, this beach would have been packed with holiday makers, and the cottage she'd managed to rent down a lane just off the seafront would have been unavailable. But she'd managed to book it at a week's notice – and on a whim. She didn't mind being alone; in fact she welcomed it.

Happy families would not have been a good vibe for her.

"You can't run away," Natalie, her colleague at the library had advised.

"I'm not running away. I'm just regrouping. I just need space to figure out what to do next."

Life had always been hectic but within the last few weeks Niall had gone off to university and Rhian was working in Australia. Then, when the library had said she would be losing her job because of cutbacks, it seemed like the last straw, and she suddenly felt she no longer served a useful purpose.

At the far end of the beach stood a ruin. Clare decided to explore it. As she approached, she suddenly saw a flash of red through one of the apertures. Someone else had had the same idea on such an inclement day, she thought.

"Hello?" she called out as she climbed up onto a grassy bank around the building. There was no reply.

She called a second time, but when she looked there was no sign of anyone. Clare frowned. Maybe she'd seen a piece of material, a lost hat or scarf perhaps, that had snagged on a rough edge. But although she searched every nook and cranny of the ruin there was not a trace of red to be found.

Continued overleaf

She supposed she could have been mistaken. She looked up. The sky was darkening and the towering cliffs seemed even more foreboding in the gloom. Waves crashed onto the rocks sending spume high into the air.

Clare felt the hairs on the back of her neck prickle. She hurried away from the ruin and back along the beach as the squall turned into a full-blown downpour.

By the time she got back to the cottage she was soaked through. There was no-one there to greet her, no Niall with his mess all over the house. She felt as sad as she'd felt at home.

That evening she went to the local pub for a meal.

"What's the building on the headland?" she asked the woman who took her order at the bar.

"It's the old salt house," the woman answered. "It hasn't been used for about 150 years, although the smugglers used to store stuff there before moving it into the caves. Have you been out there yet?"

"I went this morning," Clare said. "It's a bit eerie. I thought someone was there but no one was around."

"Oh, it was probably the ghost of old Jeremiah Rhys."

"Who's he?"

"He was the Lord of the Manor who got involved in smuggling to help the villagers. He fell in love with Marian, a local girl who was being courted by Jud Norris, a local boy.

"Jud was jealous and set them up. He called out the guard one night when he knew there was going to be a drop. Marion drowned and Jeremiah was killed in the scuffle.

"They say that if you ever see old Jeremiah's ghost, you'll be lucky in love. It's a colourful tale to tell the tourists, anyway." The woman smiled then nodded towards a corner of the room where a

man sat at a table with a laptop in front of him. "If you think you saw something, you'd better speak to Rory. He compiles all the local sightings for the website."

Clare had no intention of telling anyone else what she'd imagined that morning – she was already regretting speaking about it.

Then the woman suddenly called out, "Rory, another sighting. This lady went out to the Salt House this morning and thinks she saw something."

The man looked up. "I'd like to hear it," he said. "Why don't you join me?"

empty nest and the loss of her job.

"I'm sorry," he said. "I know what it's like when your child leaves. My son Guy is working in London."

"Do you live around here?"

"Yes. I came back after my wife died fifteen years ago."

"Oh, I'm sorry to hear that. I lost my husband ten years ago. Well, he didn't die, he just left us. It was hard to keep a roof over our heads but I managed it by getting promoted at the library. What do you do?"

"I'm a freelance journalist and I like to dabble in the local legends. I keep the

She felt that the ruins of the old Salt House didn't seem so daunting today

It would be rude to refuse now. Reluctantly Clare took a seat at his table. He seemed pleasant enough, with hair greying at his temples, a well-trimmed beard and remarkably bright blue eyes behind round-rimmed spectacles.

He smiled in welcome.

"So what did you see?"

"I thought I saw something red at a distance." Clare shrugged. "When I got there there was no one there. But it was grey and windy and raining, so I was probably mistaken."

"Old Jerry always did like to confuse people," Rory smiled warmly.

"You think it's real?"

He tapped the side of his nose, then asked, "Are you visiting the area? I've not seen you around before."

"Yes. I'm staying at Rose Cottage."

"A bit strange to be renting a holiday cottage in the middle of the winter."

She found herself telling him about her

website for the village updated." He paused. "You know, they say that Jeremiah Rhys wore a red coat."

"Please, don't say any more." Clare shivered, then she laughed. "Look at me, being spooked by ghost stories!"

"They also say that if you see his ghost you'll be lucky in love," Rory said.

"Well, that's just what I need to cheer me up," Clare said wryly.

It was brighter the next day as Clare set off for a walk along the beach. She looked off into the distance where the ruins of the Salt House stood stark against the blue sky. It didn't feel so daunting today.

Why should she be put off by ghost stories? She determined to walk as far as the ruins, wondering if she'd see something again, but convinced that she wouldn't.

Continued overleaf

Continued from previous page

But as she approached the Salt House her eye caught movement once more and her heart skipped a beat. She wasn't imagining things, surely. Somebody was there – playing a prank on her maybe.

She sped up. When she reached the ruins there was no sign of anyone.

"OK," she said out loud, sounding braver than she felt. "I know I saw something. If you're another walker and you're hiding somewhere, come out. The joke's over!"

She waited but no

helplessly while his love drowned in this very place. Suddenly she had to get away. She stumbled over the ruins and ran and ran and didn't stop until she was well clear of the Salt House.

Clare looked up from the bench on the promenade as a voice at her side startled her.

"Hello."

It was Rory.

"It's a bit cold to be sitting here, isn't it?" he said.

"I just had to catch my breath and gather my thoughts," she answered,

She found a piece of blue ceramic in a rock pool – the colour of Rory's eyes

one appeared. Then, something falling into one of the rock pools where the salt bed used to be caught her eye.

Clare clambered over the jagged wall and bent down to retrieve what looked like a piece of blue ceramic. The colour instantly reminded her of the colour of Rory's eyes, and she wondered why that should be. She turned it over in her hand then looked around.

"OK, where are you? I'm not kidding."

The only answer was the sound of the rushing sea and the screaming of gulls overhead. Maybe one of the birds had dropped it? That was the most likely explanation. Nevertheless, she felt the hairs on her neck prickling again.

She thought of Jeremiah Rhys and his love being betrayed, of him watching

putting a hand up to shield her eyes against the bright sunlight. She'd calmed down now and everything seemed normal again. "I've just been out to the ruins and had a bit of an experience again."

"Oh?" He sat down at her side.

"It isn't real, is it? It's just a ghost story for the tourists." She fingered the ceramic in her pocket.

"Well, the events really happened."

"I could have sworn someone was there – and then this appeared, seemingly out of nowhere."

She handed him the piece of ceramic.

He looked astounded.

"Do you know what Jeremiah Rhys' business was?" he said. "Pottery. Particularly blue ceramic. There were a lot of claypits in this area."

Clare laughed nervously. "Then there are probably bits lying around or buried underground and rising to the surface," she said.

"Maybe… " he mused. "How did you say you found it?"

"It was like someone threw it into a pool." She frowned. "But that sort of thing doesn't happen. The strange thing is, it made me think of your eyes – you have remarkably blue eyes…" She blushed. "I'm sorry, I'm probably being too familiar."

He smiled. "Don't worry about it. Can I make a record of this for the website and my own research?"

"If you like."

He got up. "I've got an appointment in town. Why don't you pop into the pub for a meal this evening – say seven?"

"OK." She smiled up at him.

He smiled back at her and those brilliant blue eyes twinkled.

Clare had been badly hurt by Nathan and she hadn't bothered with men ever since. It had been easier to concentrate on her children, but they were gone now and she still had the rest of her life to live.

There was something about Rory. A spark had ignited in her. But she was only here for a week, and what could happen in a week? Still, she put on something nice to meet him.

He looked delighted to see her when she turned up at seven. He wanted to know all about her, and she was curious about him too. As they talked, he didn't feel like a stranger. She felt safe as everyone in the pub knew him – they kept coming up to him and exchanging brief conversations, asking who she was and introducing themselves.

"Liz tells me you've seen Jeremiah Rhys' ghost," an older man said. "You know what they say about being lucky in love?" He winked. "And how appropriate, Rory, wouldn't you say?"

"What did he mean by that?" Clare asked when they were alone again.

"Because I'm a direct descendant of Jeremiah Rhys." Rory owned up. "I live in the big house on the cliff – his house. That's why I'm so interested in all the tales and legends."

For a moment, Clare didn't know how to respond.

"Of course, it could be coincidence," he said sheepishly.

"And who said anything about love?" She blushed.

It was another blustery day at the Salt House. This time there was no sign of any presence, no prickling of the hairs on the back of Clare's neck.

"There's no one here," she said. She turned to Rory. "Do you think there ever really was?"

"There might have been," he said. "If old Jerry is looking after us I think he brought us together. I'd like to believe the legend is true, wouldn't you?"

Clare fingered the ceramic piece in her pocket – she thought she might have it made into a pendant. Then she smiled and everything felt right as Rory reached for her free hand.

• •

MY FAVOURITE…

My favourite book is *A Man On The Moon* by Andrew Chaikin. It's a detailed account of the Apollo programme. You're there in the capsule with the astronauts every step of the way.

The Joy Of The Day

An Amish girl and a lawyer – how could it ever be?

By Pauline Saull

L eah drove the trap beneath the canopy of the large oak tree, and after tethering the horse began unloading the boxes. They contained bottled vegetables, preserved fruits, juices and seasonal fresh vegetables, all from the family farm a mile back up the road.

Leah's father had erected a rudimentary stall by the side of the road and this was where, twice a week, Leah would sell the fine foods and refreshing drinks she and her mother made; the income from this small venture being a welcome addition to the family coffers.

But for the past six weeks Leah's thoughts hadn't been centred on profit. Instead, all she could think about was the young non-Amish, or "English", man as Amish referred to them, who stopped by her stall each time she was there.

Her eyes were fixed now on a point down the road where the highway from Easington connected to the road of her stall. She knew he lived in Easington because he'd told her. She also knew his name was Rob, that he had one sister,

Continued overleaf

Connie, a dog named Blue, and that he practised law in Philadelphia, a forty-minute drive away.

Another thing Leah knew was that by having such intimate conversations with a stranger, she was breaking all the Amish laws she'd been brought up by.

Especially so because soon she would be marrying Ezekiel, their neighbour's son. A union arranged by both sets of parents with, initially, Leah's consent. But that was before she had met Rob.

She spotted his dark blue saloon turning onto the main road and her heartbeat quickened as it always did. She never ceased to marvel at the sheer joy seeing and speaking with him gave her.

Often, she told herself she was just naïve – stupid – that the answer was to work harder and look forward to becoming the wife of a goodly and gentle man. Sadly, that no longer helped because more and more, Rob took up all her thoughts.

As his car drew up and he climbed from it, she experienced an ache so sharp it almost took her breath away. *How,* she wondered, *can I possibly marry Ezekiel feeling as I do about a man I only speak with?* It was ridiculous, yet Leah knew nothing would change her feelings for Rob.

It was only in the quiet of her room at night on the days she had spoken with him, that she'd quietly voice her feelings, staring out at the star-spangled night to whisper, "I love you, Rob."

She lowered her eyes now as he approached, anxious lest he should see the desire in her eyes.

"Leah," Rob said when he reached the stall. "Lovely to see you. Did you have a good weekend?"

"Yes, thank you. Busy but productive. Mother and I did lots of bottling."

There was a short silence between them. An eagle soared overhead, emitting his high-pitched whistle and they both glanced up before Rob said, with a smile, "You've made my favourite." And he picked up a bottle of raspberry juice.

Taking a note from his wallet, he handed it over and their hands touched. In that oh-so brief tactile moment Leah experienced a strong jolt of yearning for something more, something she could not name but nevertheless wished for with all her being. The longing to let the words in her head burst from her mouth made her feel light-headed and she had to bite hard on her lip to stop them.

Oh, Rob. If only…

Just then, Sara, Ezekiel's sister trotted past in her cart. She had a stall a few yards away from Leah's where she sold pumpkin, sweet potato and corn. Leah saw her frown as she glanced their way, knew she'd witnessed the prolonged passing-over of money and wondered what she'd deduced from it.

Rob smiled at her. "I shall enjoy the juice with my lunch, and think of you."

He turned to go and Leah blurted, "Wait." Her hand closed over the note in her apron pocket, the one in which she'd told him about her dental appointment in Philadelphia in a few weeks – naming the street, in the hope he'd suggest that perhaps they could meet. But she paused, a sudden sense of fear at the step she had almost taken sweeping over her.

What had possessed her to think of putting her reputation and that of her parents at risk? And for what? A few moments' happiness speaking to a man who would certainly never understand her way of life, nor she his; a man who only bought juice from her, who probably never gave her a thought once he'd driven away? How childish she was, and how

Leah jumped, hearing Sara's voice by her side. She turned to see the petulant look on the girl's face, her eyes narrow with suspicion.

"It's the juice he enjoys, Sara," she answered. "City people are not used to such fresh produce."

"Well, Sister." Sara, tight-lipped, smoothed her apron. "Let's hope it stays that way and that his interest remains solely in the quality of your drinks. Anything else would be totally inappropriate, would it not? Aren't you seeing Ezekiel tonight for supper?"

"Yes, that's right, I am. Oh, look – you have a customer."

Her heart was beating so hard that her breath came in small gasps

compromised Rob would have felt.

"Nothing," she said. "Enjoy your day."

"Leah," Rob took a step closer to the stall again. "When I said I'll think of you when I drink this," he held up the raspberry juice, "that wasn't entirely true."

"Oh…" Leah could not keep the disappointment from her voice.

Rob smiled and she watched the tiny lines crease around his eyes. "No," he said. "In fact I think about you all the time." His face had flushed and his deep, dark brown eyes held her gaze. "I'm sorry if I've embarrassed you but I had to say it."

Abruptly he turned and walked over to his car. He climbed in, and as he drove away, he waved. Leah lifted her hand in response, her heart beating so hard her breath came in small sharp gasps.

"He spends good money with you. He never visits my stall."

Leah watched Sara hurrying away and tried to push the unwelcome thought away, that soon she and Sara would be related.

That evening over supper held at Ezekiel's parents, the mood was happy and festive with much talk between the adults over the forthcoming wedding. Sara, seated opposite Leah, kept glancing in her direction.

"You're quiet, Sister," she remarked.

Ezekiel, seated beside her, turned to face Leah. "Are you unwell?" he asked.

"No," she said truthfully, putting a hand to her head, "but I am very tired."

"Then perhaps," Sara suggested, "standing by the stall all day is becoming too much for you."

"What is this, daughter?" Leah's
Continued overleaf

mother smiled at her across the table.

"Nothing, Mother. Sara is concerned that the stall is too much for me, but that of course is nonsense."

The smile fell from her mother's face.

"Leah! Please remember your manners. We are in Sara's home."

"Yes," Ezekiel added. "I'm sure my sister only spoke out of concern for your welfare."

"I apologise, Sara." Leah pushed her chair back and stood. She had to get away. "I shall walk home," she said. "The night air

will clear my head. Thank you for a lovely supper, Mother and Father," she said to Ezekiel's alarmed-looking parents.

"Then I will accompany you." Ezekiel rose too and waited while Leah collected her cloak. "Please," he said to his parents and Leah's, "do carry on enjoying yourselves."

As they walked along the empty road Leah struggled to find ways to start a conversation. The truth was, her heart just was not in it. She wanted only to climb into bed and go over once more Rob's words to her… what they meant.

"You are not yourself these past weeks, Leah," Ezekiel observed. "I fear I am struggling to understand… have I upset you in some way?"

"Please –" Leah heard the tremor in her voice – "you must not blame yourself for my moods. Any fault lies entirely with

me. I have many doubts… worries…"

Ezekiel stopped walking and reached for her arm. The silence about them hung like a heavy cloak. Ezekiel cleared his throat. "Doubts, Leah? About what? Surely you cannot mean us? Answer me, please."

"I have no wish to hurt you," Leah whispered, "but, Ezekiel, I'm afraid I cannot marry you. It would be a sin to marry someone I didn't love, and although I am very fond of you, the love I should feel is not there. Do you understand?"

In the darkness she could see Ezekiel was smiling. He took her hand. "You silly chicken, "he said. "How you feel is quite normal, you will fall in love with me once we are married," he added confidently. "That is the way… good friends now, lovers when we marry. So, we will hear no more talk of this nature. In a very short while we will be man and wife and you will see just how ungrounded all these doubts were."

They walked the rest of the way with Ezekiel telling her of the plans he had for turning the outhouse behind his parent's property into a place Leah could make their home. He did not want, he added, to live in the big house with his family as previously planned.

"We will have our own place," he said, "with a big kitchen so that you can continue with your wonderful work preserving and bottling."

Leah lay in bed wide awake. She did not want to preserve and bottle for the rest of her life. She had a brain and wanted to use it, but just as he had been her parent's dutiful daughter she knew that as Ezekiel's equally dutiful wife there would be no opportunity for her to attend a college, widen her horizons.

His confident words had, for a moment, swayed her into thinking that yes, she could perhaps grow to love him, but it had been just that – momentary. In her heart of hearts she knew that was never going to happen. She turned onto her side and gazed at the night, allowing the pleasure of Rob's words to warm her.

I think of you all the time.

What a deliciously happy glow that gave her. But where would it lead? What could possibly happen? She was Amish,

tell me if something were amiss?"

Leah was saved from answering by her father's shout. "You forgot the tomato juice bottles, Leah."

With the stall set out, Leah sat in the folding chair and waited. Sara had arrived to set up her stall and early customers came and went, but Leah's eyes were fixed doggedly on the point further down the road – and at last, there was his dark blue saloon car.

She stepped forward eagerly, but the car didn't stop. Rob, his face tense, gave her a brief wave before carrying on toward Philadelphia.

Leah was left devastated, unable to believe it. She felt physically sick.

"He didn't bother stopping today," Sara called out from her stall.

Leah shrugged nonchalantly though

As Ezekiel's dutiful wife there would be no opportunity to widen her horizons

born into the life. Her skin prickled as her mind mulled over possible ways forward which she'd never envisaged before.

Even though she was confused and unsure, her mind was made up about one thing. Even if something prevented her from ever seeing Rob again, she would not marry a man she did not love. She would give Rob the note no matter what.

The following morning Leah rose early and filled the trap with boxes.

"Are you well now, Leah?" her mother asked anxiously. "Father and I agreed last night on our way home that you haven't been your usual cheery self just lately." She reached for her hand. "You would

her heart felt as though it might just break. The day was ruined for her and she couldn't wait for lunchtime when she had to return the trap home.

After settling the horse and unloading the empty boxes Leah glanced down the paddock where her parents were working. Both looked up and waved. She waved back before walking into the house wondering how she would get through the rest of the day without breaking down.

Rob… Rob.

Her older brother, Nathan, was sitting at the kitchen table. As Leah walked in he hurriedly pushed something into his pocket.

Continued overleaf

Continued from previous page

"Nate!" Leah's pulse raced. "Is that a phone you have there?"

He looked at her beseechingly.

"Please don't tell, Leah. It's from one of the boys I met at the lake the other day. He's non-Amish so I know I shouldn't have befriended him, but I like him. His parents bought him a new phone and so he gave this to me." He pulled the device out of his pocket and glanced across to the window. "They wouldn't like it," he said, referring to their parents.

"Let me see it." Leah held out her hand. "How does it work?"

"It's just fantastic! You can look at almost anything, speak with anyone. See, if I want to speak with Jack… that's the

here," he tapped a fingertip on his head, "is my business."

Leah nodded, for wasn't that exactly how she'd begun to feel lately? That she had a right to hope and dream… wish for things that once would have seemed impossible and undesirable. She remembered the name of the law firm Rob worked for in the city.

Later that evening after her parents had retired Leah slipped out of her room and ran along the landing to her brother's. She tapped lightly. "Nate, it's me."

He opened the door and motioned her inside. The phone was in his hand.

"What have you been looking at?" Leah whispered.

Nathan looked stricken.

"You're a good girl, Leah," her mother said. "What would I do without you?"

boy I met, I just press in the telephone number and he answers or I leave a message. Or I can send him a text."

"A text?"

"Yes. Watch. I bring up his number and type a message then press send. It's so simple."

Nathan's eyes shone with excitement and Leah felt a sense of it herself.

"So you could send a message to Philadelphia?"

Nathan laughed. "Sweet sister. You could send a message to the other side of the world should you wish to!"

Leah handed the phone back.

"Can it be our secret, Leah?"

"Secrets are sinful, are they not, Nate?"

Nathan shrugged. "Well you may think so, but I'm afraid I don't. What goes on up

"There's a college in Mornington. I could get on an agriculture course there." He sat on the bed and put his head in his hands. "Leah, I really want to do it." He looked up. "But how would the parents, our good mother and father whom I love dearly, manage without me?"

Leah sighed. "I don't know. Remember when Matthew Tranter left home? Everyone thought his parents would never get over it, but," she added, "they had in their favour the benefit of their undying faith. As I believe ours would, should such a thing happen. You have to do what you think is best for yourself, Nate. You're only twenty-two and if this is not the life for you, well…" Leah's voice trailed off.

"I believe you're right." Nathan looked at the phone. "Good or evil?" he asked.

Leah smiled. "Let's say interesting instead. Could you… could you look up on there the name of a law firm for me?"

"Law firm?" Nathan grinned. "Not thinking of becoming a lawyer, are you?"

Leah lay beneath the quilt her grandmother had made and ran her hand over the raised star in the middle. Her pulse raced even though she was resting, for Nathan had easily found the name of Rob's company with its telephone number listed.

Not only that, it gave a list of all the lawyers employed there with their respective email addresses. All you had to do, Nathan told her, was click on *Mailbox*, type a message and press send. It was that simple. So she now had the means to contact Rob…

Yet how could she do that when he'd driven past her with only a casual wave? And what would she say anyway?

No. It was ridiculous. Better stop thinking about herself and concentrate on her brother's problems instead. She slipped out of bed and knelt beside it, saying a fervent prayer for the best outcome for her brother and parents. She loved them all and wanted only the best for them.

The following day Leah spent with her mother in the kitchen. There were bottles and jars to sterilise which would be filled with the vegetable and mustard pickles already made. They worked without stopping for lunch.

The room was hot even with the windows and door open. Leah watched her mother wipe a hand across her damp brow, noted the strands of hair sticking to her neck, and reaching across, took the ladle from her.

"Sit down a while, Mother," she said. "I will do that."

"You're a good girl, Leah." Her mother sank into the old rocking chair. "What would I do without you?'

As Leah worked, the words rang in her head. What absurd ideas she'd been harbouring about a life for herself… indeed, even going to college. It was impossible when her mother needed her.

Yet even as she acknowledged that fact, while she finished the bottling and **Continued overleaf**

Continued from previous page

crating ready for the morning, her stomach churned with a mixture of excitement and apprehension.

Would she see him? Would he stop to speak with her? *Oh, please, yes!*

She glanced at her mother sleeping in the rocker and went into the larder. On the shelf were the last of the raspberry juices. She collected them and put them with the vegetables.

"Yes." Leah saw Sara making her way over from her own stall and quickly reached for a bottle of juice, her other hand going to her apron pocket. She handed the note and bottle to Rob.

He took them wordlessly, his eyes never leaving hers.

"Thank you," he said softly before walking away.

"That was a quick visit," Sara remarked. "I was hoping for an

She handed him the bottle of juice – and the note from her apron pocket

The morning was warm with a soft breeze coming from the south. Leah was feeding the horse an apple when she saw Rob's car turn onto the highway.

"Oh!" She dropped the apple and ran to the stall, her heart beating so hard she feared it would burst through her ribs. And as she'd wished for all that long sleepless night, the blue sedan slowed and stopped and Rob climbed out.

Leah was so relieved tears welled in her eyes. She whispered his name to herself, watching as he walked toward her, his gaze fixed on her face.

"Hello, Leah," he said quietly when he stood close. "I… er, I…" He pushed a hand through his hair. "I have to apologise. I thought it might have upset you, when I said… well, that I perhaps spoke out of turn, and so I was too embarrassed to stop the other day. I am so sorry…"

"Rob! No, you must not think that," Leah exclaimed. "Your words made me happier than I can say."

He stared at her. "Really?"

introduction." She smiled slyly. "He's very handsome."

"And I'm very busy." Leah turned away to smile at the woman approaching her stall. From the corner of her eye, she saw the blue car drive off.

She had added to her note, *I have sent you an email message. I don't know how long the phone will last, but for now you can, if you wish, reply. Leah.*

Would he contact her? Leah didn't know for certain – but for now, with the expectation that, yes, he might, she was walking on air.

Whatever the consequences of her actions they would have be dealt with by her alone, but for now nothing, no one, could take the absolute joy out of her day.

MY FAVOURITE...

My favourite film has to be *Out of Africa*, starring Meryl Streep and Robert Redford, for the nostalgia it evokes of a bygone age – and of course, the sheer gorgeousness of its setting.

FANCY THAT!

Fascinating Facts **On Water!**

✦ There is an old, abandoned Russian cruise ship that has been roaming international waters since 2011.

✦ During WW2 a Dutch ship was disguised as a tropical island to avoid detection by the Japanese!

 ✦ In 2013 the chef of a sunken ship survived for 3 days by taking refuge in an air pocket of the upturned ship.

✦ A ship named Baychimo abandoned off the coast of Alaska in 1931 was spotted still adrift in the Arctic in 1969.

✦ Chunosuke Matsuyama, a Japanese seaman, sent a message in a bottle in 1784 saying that his ship had been wrecked. It washed up in the village where he had been born... in 1935!

✦ **Approximately 17,000 ships use the Suez Canal every year.**

✦ Sarah Breton made history in 2010 as the first female cruise ship captain.

A whopping 90% of the world's trade goods are carried by sea

✦ In 1838, Edgar Allan Poe wrote a novel where shipwrecked survivors ate one of their own, called Richard Parker. 46 years later the Mignonette sank and the four survivors ate the cabin boy – Richard Parker. The story inspired the movie, *Life of Pi*.

✦ In 2004, a study found that retiring to a cruise ship is as cost-effective as a retirement home and provides a better quality of life.

✦ **The largest cruise ship is the Royal Caribbean liner Oasis of the Seas, at 225,000 tonnes and 400 yards long.**

✦ An intact steamboat from 1856 was excavated in 1988 from a farmer's field. The artefacts were so well preserved that some of the food was still edible.

The True Value Of Things

Everyone in your life leaves something behind, even if you don't appreciate its value until much later…

By Michelle Matthews

Mum?" Ciara says as she pokes her head around the door. "Yes?" I ask brightly, trying to cover my sadness as I sort through piles of clothes.

"Oooh, that's nice!"

"Would you like it?"

"It'll never fit me."

She's right. She's nearly a foot taller than I am, my beautiful, brainy daughter.

I turn to look down at the socks I'm sorting, so that she won't see the tears that I can't stop from filling my eyes.

Honestly, it's just as bad as her first day of school. Yet, look at how wonderfully she's done since then, graduating from dentistry last June, and ready to start her first job at the local dental surgery next week.

In the meantime, for these last four months, she's been living at home with me. I always thought she might return for a bit after university, but this time, when she moves out, I know it will be for good.

"Have you ever thought of selling some of these things on eBay?" she asks.

"No. It sounds like too much trouble."

"It's not, really."

"Have you done it before?" I straighten up, tears finally under control.

"I've sold a few things. I've actually just made a pile of my old clothes that could be sold, and I wondered if you had anything you'd like to add to it?"

I look at the three-foot-high stack of dresses, trousers, coats, shirts, and so forth on my bed, some dating back twenty years, and nod.

"Only… Ciara, let's make a deal – whatever money we make, we spend on something special. No more random retail therapy. Not after putting in all this effort to clear out and put our home in order."

"It's a deal." Ciara laughs, then scoops up a bunch of things from my bed and disappears back to her room.

So it carries on all weekend. We go through our clothes, our books, our magazines, DVDs, kitchen utensils and cooking supplies, even the hopelessly cluttered cupboard under the stairs.

Ciara takes charge of the items she says we can sell, and I make several trips to the charity shop.

I don't tell her that, after the first trip, I had to stop for a cup of tea at the nearest **Continued overleaf**

café to regain my composure. It's so hard to say goodbye to all of these things, especially Ciara's old toys. Well, all right, I've secreted some away, just in case I have grandchildren one day. And the novels I used to escape into when life wasn't going according to plan. And, yes, I did bring a few favorites back home, promising myself that I'll read them again.

All weekend, whenever my resolve to part with things wavers, I tell myself firmly that it's the memories rather than the things that are worth keeping. If that doesn't quite work, I remind myself that congratulating ourselves on all of our hard work.

"All grown up, having a glass of wine with my little girl," I say, laughing bravely.

I don't tell her what a relief it is to see her, twenty-three years old, settled into a really good job, and living only a twenty-minute walk away.

I don't tell her how worried I've been for the last five years, while she was away at university. You hear so many sad stories of what can go wrong at that age, what with alcohol or drugs or assault – or simply failing exams and having to leave. But Ciara made it through safely, and

I tell myself firmly it's memories rather than things that are worth keeping

everything will make its way to a good home, and raise money for a good cause along the way.

By the last trip, I don't exactly feel happy, but I do feel a sense of lightness, even excitement. After all, Ciara and I are both preparing for a new life.

Sunday night finds us collapsed on the sofa, in a home that's never been so tidy. It feels ready for whatever the future may bring into it, I reflect, as we're both enjoying a glass of wine and

she's even come home, much to my surprise and delight.

"Mum?" she says tentatively. "We've done a brilliant job this weekend."

"Yes, we have."

"But… there's still one thing we haven't dealt with…"

I know exactly what she means, but I play for time by saying, "Oh, is there?" *Perhaps she'll let it go*, I think.

She doesn't. In a rush, she says, "I really think we need to go into the loft and look at the things Dad left behind."

"Oh."

"I'm here until the end of the week. It's… well, it's important to me."

"Right." I'm slightly annoyed. How could I refuse her? I know she probably needs closure – just as much as I do – but I feel as though she's cornered me.

"Well, I suppose we could start on all

that tomorrow?" she suggests, sensing my reluctance.

"That sounds sensible," I agree.

That night, I lie awake. Ciara's dad wasn't around much when she was growing up. I fell pregnant with her soon after he and I were married, and it was pretty obvious from the first week after her arrival that fatherhood wasn't going to come naturally to him – or at all, as it turned out.

I felt like such a fool! How could I have not realised this before we were married?

We had discussed having children. Looking back, I could see that his attitude had been, at best, neutral. He confessed, years later, that he'd never wanted children, but had hoped he might feel differently after we had one.

In fact, the opposite had happened. Then, one day, when Ciara was only a year old, I sent him to the shops for nappies… and that was that.

Not that I figured it out right away. I remember it got dark outside, and I kept waiting for the telephone to ring, or for the police to knock on the door. I was worried he'd been involved in some sort of freak accident. I mean, who walks out on a baby like that?

I eventually called my mum, who came over. Bless her, she didn't say a single unkind word. She just helped with Ciara. I would have gone under without her.

She'd just retired from thirty years of teaching, and I'm sure she had dreams of globe-trotting, but she stayed. I promised myself I'd be the same with my little girl.

Still, it broke my heart daily, all the little things she missed out on. I remember her coming home from school one day, having defiantly written *Happy Grandmother's Day* on the Father's Day cards she'd made. I don't know if the other kids teased her much – it isn't so uncommon to be raised by a single parent these days – but I still felt guilty, even though I wasn't the one who'd left.

Then he came back, out of the blue, when she was ten. I was furious.

I didn't let him move in, but I did decide to let him spend time with Ciara, after discussing it with her. It was what she wanted.

After that, he came and went. His departures always left her sad, but she was terribly grown-up about it. He usually came bearing presents. When Ciara left for university, I packed them all away in the loft. But I know that Ciara's right – we have to deal with these things.

So, are you still in touch with your dad?" I ask briskly, too cheerfully.

We've climbed into the cramped loft, and are dragging the boxes of stuff nearer the trapdoor.

"Off and on. You know what he's like."

"I'm sorry you had such a crap dad."

"It's not your fault."

I shrug. I'll always feel as though it is. I

Continued overleaf

should have chosen a better man. But then, I wouldn't have had this one particular, amazing daughter, would I?

One by one, we bring the boxes downstairs, me passing them down to her. We go through everything.

"Look, this is a photo of us at the beach," she says, showing me a frozen-in-time remnant of a day out they'd had when she was eleven.

"I'm sorry, I've never said thanks, Mum," she says.

"What do you mean?" I ask.

"Thanks for letting me get to know him. I must have been hard for you."

"It was. Most of the time, I wanted to shove him in the canal! But I realised

them in a small album. It does feel cathartic, letting it all go.

Except that it turns out that we're not quite done. On her last evening at home, I'm in the kitchen, stirring the fish soup Mum taught me to make years ago.

I hear Ciara behind me.

"Mum – is this what I think it is?" she asks me.

I turn to see her holding out her hand, palm up. On it, there is a slender gold ring with a tiny yet clear, sparkling diamond.

"Oh!" I exclaim. I had honestly forgotten about my wedding ring.

"I found it at the bottom of one of the boxes. It was under some baby books."

I remember now…

I'd been packing up the books Ciara

"I'm fine," I tell her, "but I don't want this any more," and I give her the ring

that it was the only fair thing to do for you – although I worried so much about you getting hurt."

She nods, putting the photo aside.

"I kind of knew not to get my hopes up with him. He's doing the best that he can, I told myself. He's rubbish, but if rubbish is the best he can manage, then that's the best he can manage."

I laugh. "That's very wise of you."

"I'm glad that *your* best was so much better, though."

I smile, trying to keep those tears at bay again, and lean over to hug her.

"The feeling is mutual," I tell her.

In the end, we get rid of most of the things he gave her over the years. She gathers up the photos with a plan to put

had outgrown, and the council tax bill had arrived, and I'd known I'd have to ask Mum for help paying it. I felt so helpless – and angry. Why wasn't he here? Couldn't he at least send money?

I'd torn off my ring, wondering why I was still wearing it when my husband had been gone six months. I chucked it in the box with the books and packed it all away.

Now, I pick up the ring. It's so tiny. My hands have changed so much, becoming stronger and, frankly, careworn over the years. I could never wear it now, even if I wanted to.

"Are you… are you OK?" Ciara asks.

I consider this, and realise that, yes, actually I am OK. I'm not angry any more – or hurt, or afraid.

"I'm fine," I say, meeting her gaze.

"But I don't want this any more."

I give the ring to her and turn back to stirring the soup. I can feel Ciara watching me closely, before she quietly leaves the kitchen.

Three months later and Ciara's busy with her work, but I still see her more often than I did when she was at university. One afternoon, she comes over, a broad smile on her face.

"Mum, I have something for you." She hands over a tiny box.

I stare at it. It's from Gilbert's, the posh jeweller on Grosvenor Street. We used to look in the window and admire all the pretty things.

I lift the lid. Inside is nestled the most beautiful pendant necklace, with three tiny jewels – an emerald, a sapphire, and an amethyst – all set within the petals of a white-gold rose.

"Our birthstones," I breathe.

"Do you like it?" she asks nervously.

"Oh, it's beautiful – but how could you afford it?" I know she's doing well, but she has student loans, and she's trying to save up for her own home.

"Remember all that stuff we sold on eBay? It really added up. Also, I…" She hesitates. "I took your ring to Gilbert's and had it appraised. It turns out that diamond was actually pretty valuable."

"Really?" I'm astonished.

"Really. You don't mind, do you?"

"Mind what? That you sold it? No, darling, not at all."

"No, I mean, because I used the money to have this necklace made, which kind of… makes it from him, in a way."

I mull this over. The stones in the pendant glitter – amethyst for Mum, sapphire for Ciara, and emerald for me.

I'm flooded with memories… first of the struggles and the loneliness, but then of laughter and hugs… memories of Mum teaching me to make her famous fish soup… of reading Ciara stories before bed… of the three of us planting wild roses in my tiny patch of garden… and of the three of us celebrating Ciara's graduation last June.

No, you could never say Ciara's father gave me what I'd hoped for in life, but he did, without knowing it, bring a lot of love and wonder into my life. Surprisingly – like the diamond.

"No, darling, I think this is wonderful," I tell my daughter.

She beams. "Let me help you put it on."

She does, and I wear it every day, this reminder of my daughter, my mother, and myself, all growing together.

● ●

MY FAVOURITE…

O Brother, Where Art Thou? **is my favourite film. I love it for its atmosphere, its eccentricity and for proving George Clooney can act as well as look gorgeous.** *Sally Rodger, Deputy Editor*

Busy Hands

My aunt had been more than a little houseproud…

By Pamela Pickton

Somehow I don't think she wants me in her house – my distant relative, my aunt, for some time departed this life as well as this house.

Her portrait above the mantelpiece looks down on me as I get up from the floor where I have been watching television, and drop onto her carpet the crumbs from the far too many biscuits I have been eating.

I wish in a way that I had known the lady who used to live here: aunt of my second cousin, my second cousin twice removed, or whatever she was.

That is the trouble with a family which is dwindling; the lady had no nearer relative than me. It seems wrong, the way it goes sometimes, doesn't it? The way some fairly idle and certainly profligate young person is suddenly handed a couple of hundred thousand as the only, though many times removed, relative of some poor old man, who had always been materially self-denying?

Of course had the poor old man made a will, he might have left his money to someone more deserving or more in need, or just someone he would have preferred to have had it. But then the nearest blood relative could always contest that will, couldn't they?

At the moment, I think the closest person to inherit from me is some young second niece a million times removed. I don't know her, I have never seen her, but

do I want to bother? I am not thinking of going anywhere for a long time yet.

Yet, in a way, I *do* know the old aunt or cousin who owned this house. I can tell that she was very houseproud; the polish in this place is nothing to do with a quick clean-up by an agency before the handover to me. It feels that the love of

decades is layer-deep in all the furniture; and there are many invisible layers of protective shine, like an aura, around the unscratched windows and perfectly silvered mirrors.

At first, I felt that she must have had help. True, I was bequeathed only
Continued overleaf

Continued from previous page
property, not income, but of course she may have had means which died with her.

But now that I am gradually integrating in the surrounding community and the church, I learn that Miss Edgerton did indeed do everything herself. And in fact her enthusiasm about housework was almost an obsession.

"She would not have had some stranger in her home to clean, touching her things," I have been told. And some say that is why she never married; she would not have wanted some man or child messing up her place. Which I suppose is why I wonder how she feels if she is watching me – biscuit crumbs and all.

Oh – and apparently she had told one close friend that sex and childbirth were far too messy, and would disrupt her

kitchen, but I feel she is watching me wherever I go in this house.

Perhaps I just feel guilty. Not very nice to die, is it, and have someone else in your house, using everything?

Still, she is not looking really… is she? I am no domestic and have no money for a char. Better wring the cloth out properly, though. Once, when I just threw it down on the draining board, all soapy and even a bit greasy, I swear I felt a cold slap on the wrist.

Back to the polishing, I suppose. I am slovenly at heart, I know. Maybe that is a bit harsh. Lazy, perhaps. Or slipshod? Yes, that is the word. You see, sometimes, when I do half the cleaning and leave the rest for tomorrow, I leave all the brushes and dusters and things in a corner somewhere. Who's to know, I ask myself,

As I threw a cloth on the draining board, I swear I felt a cold slap on the wrist

routines! I often think of that as I put on my make-up and look at the smears of foundation and spilled blusher all over her lovely dressing table.

It seems fair reward that I should be here, after years in a non-pensioned job, and looking after my parents, but on the other hand this is a big place to look after.

I was never the housewifey sort; it was as much as I could do to go to work and look after Mum and Dad. I've been glad of flat-shares these last few years.

Oh, well, I have been eating lunch while having that little brood. Must clear everything away and wipe the table down. Aunt Gert's picture is not in the

and it saves the time and energy of walking to the broom cupboard to put it away only to fetch it out again next day.

Well! I must be improving. Picking up Aunt Gert's influence or something. No cloth or polish in that corner. In the cupboard after all!

Oh! The polish is nearly all gone. Funny, because I've not been here very long, and I don't clean that often. A bit heavy-handed with it, perhaps? I always think an extra dollop of any cleaning agent makes for less elbow grease.

It's a good excuse to nip down to the village shops: I need some new blusher and, well, why not look at the ads in the newsagents? I can't afford to retire under age; maybe a little part-time job would get me out of the place a bit more. Slap on the wrist, indeed!

Come to that, maybe someone wants lodgings too. With a little job and a lodger, why, I could even run to a cleaning lady.

Of course, if the lodger were a lady, she may even clear up after herself: one of those women I have met who say that to them, housework is as natural as breathing!

I'd rather it were a man, or course, to help with the garden and heavy jobs. And… it's never too late for anything, they say, don't they?

I am just lazy about practical things, that's the truth. Putting my coat away after shopping, I remember how one of my flat share-friends used to tear her hair out at the way I put things on hangers: several things on one, wire ones tangled up, and – worst crime of all – the garment thrown on crookedly, not fitting onto the shoulders and the buttons not done up.

I know how Aunt Gert did it; some of her clothes had been left where she kept them, in a spare wardrobe. That must have been missed by whoever cleared her personal effects.

She died in the winter and I suppose her coats and woollies were in the main bedroom where I sleep now. But in the closet of another bedroom, I found her summer ones; jackets, neat linen dresses and suits for church, all buttoned up, straightened on padded hangers, all brushed free of hairs and fluff.

Anyway, no luck on the notice board. The trip didn't take long. Maybe I should get on with the polishing. Or sort my clothes cupboard out.

But, then, it`s nearly tea time. And there`s that soap on TV. *I'll do the polishing tomorrow*, I think as I come down from putting my coat away, and swivel myself round, hand on the banister end, towards the kitchen and afternoon tea.

With a shudder, I realise that once I would not have put my coat away, bundled or otherwise. I would have left it at the end of the stairs.

She`s really taking me over, I think, all the more determined to make tea, have it in front of the television, with toast, and drop the crumbs on the floor.

Polishing the table rather half-heartedly **Continued overleaf** the next day, I feel my rubbing with the duster getting fiercer. It is almost as though someone has a grip on my wrist.

Oh, rubbish! I really must get a job.

But if not her or another ghost, there is certainly some influence in this house. Or is it that the house remembers and is making me tidier? I catch myself putting my coat away every time and, after a few days, I notice that every single item in the wardrobe is properly arranged on its hanger, hanging separately from everything else.

About to do the polishing the following week, I am glad to get a call from a new village friend inviting me round for a cup

the dishcloth wrung out and hanging over the taps but the tea towel and hand towels neatly, geometrically, folded on their rail.

Now, I may well have hung them up, but I would never have made exact oblongs of them like that.

I go to the library and take out various books on matters spiritual, psychological, and even about hallucination. Then I find one on exorcism.

It takes me days just to skim through them all. During that time I put clothes correctly on hangers and fold cloths and towels edge-to-edge with knife pleats. And I polish like a crazy person. If I am going to find those things done, I have to know that it is I who have done them.

Is there a ghost inside me? That is the most frightening thought of all

of tea. Morning coffee time really, but tea more suited to her wanting me to try a slice of home-made cake.

Good. I can leave the wretched cleaning. I grab a jacket and rebelliously leave the duster and tin of polish in the middle of the beautiful oak dining table.

Back from tea, I am greeted by a waft of lavender furniture polish. Shaking, I walk to the dining room and see that the duster and tin are no longer there. I steel myself to look in the broom cupboard and, in shock, stagger to the kitchen for strong coffee – or something stronger – already wondering if I have gone mad.

Did I finish the polishing before my friend called, and put the things back?

Waiting for the kettle to boil and hunting for some whisky, I see not only

At last, I have made a plan. The house is looking beautiful; loved, as Gertrude Edgerton would have wanted. I have a fire blazing for the first time, have brought in leaves and berries and bought a potted flowering plant.

I light a candle and play a CD on meditation, which I got from the library too. From all I have read, this seems the best way. I ask her gently to leave. I promise to look after the house as she would have wanted. But I want to be here on my own. It is my turn now.

I no longer know whether she has gone or I have changed. The coats and jackets are always hanging properly in the wardrobe, never left on the banisters. The tea towels are always folded neatly, if not edge to edge.

I still eat meals in front of the

television, and I am not always careful about dropping bits. But I do get the carpet sweeper out afterwards. Kind of automatically.

Mind you, if a friend calls me with a sudden invitation, I always go and leave the housework. True, I do put the cleaning things away first. But maybe that is again because I want to know that *I* did it.

Is there a ghost in the house… or is there a ghost inside me? That is the most frightening thought of all.

But oh, come on. I do forget things. Look, I am still the lazy person I always have been. For example, when tidying downstairs, instead of taking upstairs things which belong there, I leave them at the bottom of the stairs to be taken up when I have reason to go up, or last thing at night.

Or tomorrow.

Sometimes there are things on several stairs, even going half way up.

And I am always so forgetful when I am out shopping. I become so absorbed in trying to find a job and a lodger – or a bit of make-up – that, even though I take them out with me every time, I forget to take those old house-shoes to the menders. The heel is nearly off. Slipshod, me – quite literally.

No – no prim Gertie, me. Why have I not taken that photograph down? I still wear my make-up, still fancy my chances. There's a whist drive tonight at the church, where I have met a couple of fairly young, recently widowed, men.

I am upstairs now, changing my dress, at the tidy wardrobe, as the phone rings.

I keep forgetting to get that upstairs extension fitted – *see, I am still me,* I reassure myself as I fly down the stairs. It could be one of those nice men calling to offer me a lift tonight.

Oh… I took everything else up, but left that pile half way up the stairs, unsure what I was going to do with them. A pile of glossy, slithery magazines.

Drat these shoes.

Oh…!

The phone's stopped ringing, I missed that boat. I feel funny, dizzy; it must be the excitement. Perhaps he – whoever – will ring again.

I steady myself on the banister and walk to the kitchen, yet again, for a stiff drink. In the doorway I stop dead.

"What are you doing here?" I shout, but she doesn't hear me.

Who is this young woman, standing there washing up at my sink?

She tosses the dishcloth into the dirty washing-up water and turns away. I go to rescue it, but she doesn't see me.

I don't think I want this new young girl in my house.

● ●

MY FAVOURITE…

My favourite film is *Chariots Of Fire* because it is about human endeavour, never giving up. It also features some of the songs of my beloved Gilbert and Sullivan.

There's No Looking Back

With a little encouragement anything was possible, as Millie found out when she was in a tight spot…

By Tracy Baines

Millie turned left and drove up the street, oblivious of the dead-end sign, bringing the car to an abrupt halt at the newly erected bollards that now divided one end of Dolphin Street from the other.

Cars lined either side of the narrow street and a quick glance in the rear view mirror revealed it was like that all the way back to the main road. How did that happen? Panic set in. She was rubbish at three-point turns. How was she going to get out of this?

The car stalled and she slumped in her seat, mind racing. She'd have to stay there until the other cars left. Or attempt a kamikaze 47-point turn, hitting the other cars like dodgems! Her no claims bonus would go for sure.

Gary was right. She was useless. She checked her watch. She'd never make the interview now, even though she'd left in plenty of time – and though she'd had Gary putting forward all sorts of reasons why she shouldn't

even bother. She'd tried to assert herself. Her mum and her friends had attempted to fill her full of confidence, but Gary's voice was the loudest, niggling away like a dripping tap wearing away stone. She had to turn off that tap.

She took a deep breath. She wasn't going to be defeated, had to prove to herself she could do this.

She restarted the engine, put the gears into reverse. The clutch screeched as it failed to engage. Her hand shook with the vibration and she put it back into neutral. All her confidence was slipping away.

She inhaled, let out a low deep breath. *Stay calm*, she told herself, *you won't be able to think clearly if you panic*. She was relieved there wasn't an audience to witness her incompetence. She got out of the car. Was anyone going to move, create a gap so that she could at least attempt a three point turn? It was too far to reverse – she was rubbish at that as well.

A curtain twitched. She got back into the car. She had to try, she had to make that interview.

She contemplated calling for **Continued overleaf**

Thoughtful

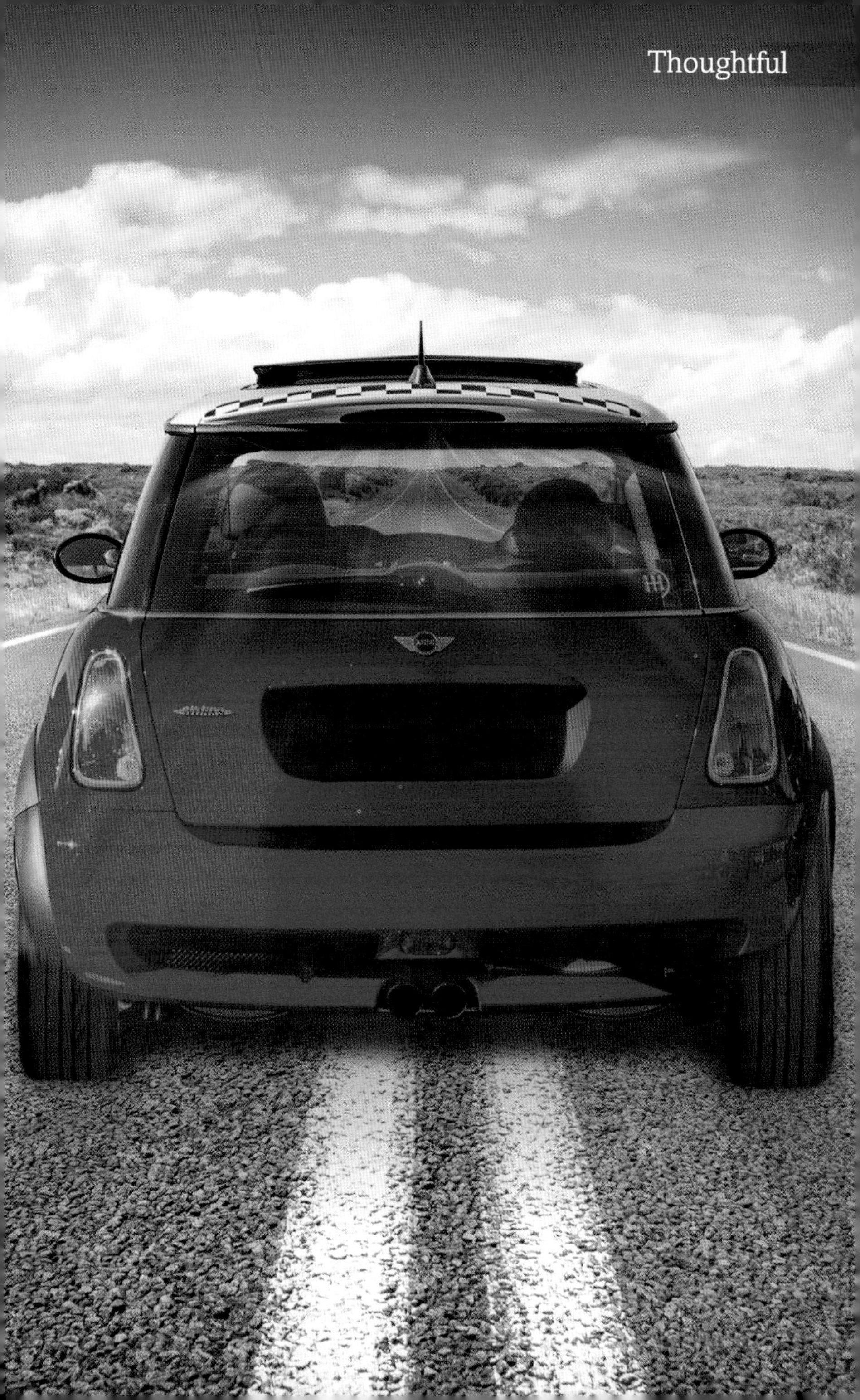

Thoughtful

Continued from previous page

help. Was this worthy of the RAC? Probably not. Gary would be there like a shot if she phoned, but the last thing she wanted was to have him gloating.

She thought about the poor woman who had tried for half an hour to reverse park and ended up on YouTube, a laughing stock. She shuddered, checked for likely culprits with mobile phones. The curtain twitched again and she slunk further down in her seat, wishing she could disappear.

She'd have to call Gary. She was scrolling through the numbers on her phone when someone tapped sharply on her window.

A woman in her seventies was indicating for her to wind down the window. She braced herself for a barrage of abuse. Blocking the street, whatever next, she shouldn't be in charge of a car!

Instead the woman said, "This happens all the time, dear, since they put those bollards up. Sat Navs haven't got the message yet. I've reported it to the council. Can I help?"

Millie looked at her phone, Gary's number displayed, then looked again at the woman. It was worth a try. She threw the phone down on the passenger seat.

"If you could watch me either side, I could reverse."

"Of course." The woman smiled cheerily. "This is my new full-time job. I've had plenty of practice." She leaned in at the window. "Do you want to reverse the whole way or do a three-point turn when there's a gap?"

"Is there a gap?" Millie was hopeful.

The woman stood erect, peered around, leaned back in. "A fair way up, but there's a ramp to a builder's yard, that

should be clear. Just take it easy, one bit at a time, and stop if you get tired."

She smiled warmly and Millie began to feel more capable. She might need help to do this but she *could* do it.

Once more Millie put the car into reverse, and began to move slowly back, all the time the woman's voice coming through the open window… "Straighten up a little, left hand down… slowly, slowly… that's fine, you're doing well."

It was so soothing, being encouraged. It seemed that in no time at all Millie was beside the entrance to the builder's yard, where she reversed in and turned the car to point along in the opposite direction.

"Well done," said the woman as Millie leaned across the passenger seat.

"I couldn't have done it without you." Millie smiled. "Thank you so much."

The woman waved a dismissive hand. "Nonsense, you did it all on your own, you just didn't trust yourself."

"Thanks anyway," Millie said. She checked her watch. There was still time to make the interview and oddly enough, she felt more confident about it now. The old lady was right, she was distracted by the other cars – just as she was distracted by other voices, especially Gary's.

She looked in the rear view mirror and the woman waved as she moved off. She waved back, smiling. Sometimes dead ends could be a new way forward if you had the right encouragement, and if you did, there was no looking back.

●●●●●●●●●●●●●●●●●●●●●●●●●●●

MY FAVOURITE…

I loved the first *Home Alone* film when it came out – and I still love watching it now, along with my children!
Karen Milne, picture researcher

Brain BOOSTERS

Sudoku 1   Sudoku 2

Fill in each of the blank squares with the numbers 1 to 9, so that each row,
each column and each 3x3 cell contains all the numbers from 1 to 9.

Sudoku 1

		2		7		8		
			8		6		2	
		5				1		
1		2		5				7
	6			8			4	1
4			9	1		2		
	9			4				8
6		3		5				
	4		8	7		1		

Sudoku 2

						8		3
			3	8	5		9	
					4			
	2		1					5
	8				3	1	6	
	1	7				4		
4				7	8	1		
	9			1				4
7			6	4			5	

Word Wheel

Turn To Page 143 For Solutions

You have ten minutes to find as many
words as possible using the letters in
the wheel. Each word must be three
letters or more and contain the
central letter. Use each letter once
and no plurals, foreign words or
proper nouns are allowed. There
is at least one nine-letter word.

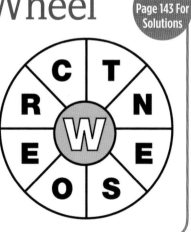

Average: 38 words
Good: 39-57 words
Excellent: 58-75 words

Ice Cream With Sparkles

It's often the trivial little things that can make it seem life is worth living again after all…

By Frances Chambers

Carefully I opened the pink envelope addressed to Miss Hayley Tipton, Top Flat, 6 Otter Close. Inside was a *Welcome to Your New Home* card from Mum and Dad with a pretty picture of lilac and roses.

Mum had written, *All our love, darling. Just ring if you feel a bit low. We're always here.*

Caught off-guard, I felt that familiar ache. *Peter!* I hadn't meant it to be like this; we had been planning our lives together, not apart. But then Peter had been offered a promotion to his firm's head office in America.

At first I was uncertain about such a big move but gradually I became excited by the idea of life in Boston.

"It will be an adventure!" I said.

He agreed but he didn't sound convinced and gradually I noticed with prickles of anxiety that he had stopped talking about "we" and "us". I realised that I wasn't going with him – he was leaving me behind.

"Why?" I asked him. "Why? Don't you love me any more?"

I never got a true answer. He just seemed to have changed; he had become tougher and harder, talking about his career and how opportunities had to be grasped because they might not come again, and how in business there wasn't room for being sentimental.

I heard later that he had a new girlfriend in America – someone who for the last six months had been working at his London office.

He left me a note when he went.

I realised that we weren't right for each other. It wouldn't have worked out, but I wish you all the luck in the world. Peter.

All this came rushing back to me now as I stood holding Mum and Dad's card.

I loved the flat; it was small and right at the top of the house. The ceilings sloped and the floor sloped and you had to climb three flights of stairs to get up there, but it had a view from the small-paned windows of slated roofs and gardens and lots of sky.

And it was all mine; a new flat, a new job, a new life. No more Peter, no more crying into my pillow when he didn't come home until two am, no more twisting my engagement ring around my finger and wondering why everything had gone so very wrong.

I had no furniture because nothing

from my and Peter's house, and nothing my parents could offer me, would fit into the flat or could even be dragged up the stairs. So because I didn't have much money, I started going to Saturday household auctions.

The first time I went, I stood at the back and was too nervous to bid. I kept my hands in my pockets, frightened that I might find I'd bought a Victorian dolls' house or a set of carpenter's tools but by the third week I had got the hang of things. In fact, I thoroughly enjoyed rootling through the lots at the viewing on Friday nights and discovering something **Continued overleaf**

Continued from previous page

which would look just right in the flat.

I got a small pine table and three chairs which I sanded down and painted blue-grey to match the sky through the windows. I got mix-and-match cups and saucers and plates, I got a small sofa, I covered cushions and stitched curtains.

Finally I got a chest of drawers. It was the right size to fit beneath the slope of the ceiling, and it was perfect for the bedroom. I looked at it and felt happy, which I hadn't felt in ages.

There was just one thing. The chest of drawers was painted white with pink handles and it had flower fairies stencilled across the top. It must have belonged

"Oh…" I said. "Hello, I'm Hayley. Is the chest of drawers pink and white?"

"Yes – with fairies."

"Is there a problem?"

"Well, not with the chest itself – but have you looked inside?"

I hadn't.

"We think Old Ted may be in there. He's our daughter Rosie's teddy, she's had him since she was a baby. I'm so sorry."

"No, no, don't worry," I said. "I'll just go and have a look."

Sure enough, Old Ted had hidden himself away in the bottom drawer.

"Oh, thank goodness!" Maxine said. "Will it be all right if I get Graham to call round after work to pick him up?"

Making my way up the long flights of stairs, I felt sadness wash through me

to a child – a little girl. Caught suddenly by memories of the family Peter and I had planned, my eyes filled with tears.

Pete had wanted boys, I longed for a daughter. As I looked at the dancing fairies, all the hurt came flooding back. No pink ballet tights, no footballs in the garden, no frog wellies, no Christmas stockings, no chocolate button cakes… the tears rolled down my cheeks.

The phone rang and, trying to catch my sobs, I hurried to the sitting room.

A pleasant-sounding woman's voice said, "I'm Maxine Hughes and I'm so sorry to bother you." She sounded about my age. "I hope you don't mind but the auctioneer gave me your phone number. I believe you bought our daughter's chest of drawers this morning?"

At six o'clock I hurried down the stairs to hand Ted to the nice-looking man standing in the porch.

"I'm Graham Hughes," he said. "I think Maxine explained? Rosie has been really missing Ted."

"How old is she?" I couldn't help asking.

"Nearly six. And then there's Liam as well and he's two, so between them they're quite a handful."

"Yes," I said, "they must be."

I had tried to keep my voice bright and cheerful, but when I closed the door and was making my way slowly up the long flights of stairs, I felt sadness wash through me once more.

A girl and a boy – how lucky was Maxine! And lucky, too, to have Graham, who clearly was kind and responsible and proud of his family.

The following Saturday morning, the downstairs doorbell rang. On the step I found a small girl clutching Old Ted. Behind her stood a smiling woman about my age with a little boy in a buggy.

"Ted wants you to come to my birthday party," the little girl said, looking back to her mum to make sure she'd got the message right.

"I'm Maxine, this is Rosie and this is Liam," her mum said smiling. "And I hope you are Hayley? It's Rosie's party today and we would love you to come."

So I went along to Rosie's sixth birthday party and found that the family lived just around the corner from me.

When Maxine opened the door, holding Liam on her hip, I found Graham organising ten small girls in a game of musical bumps. Shrieks and laughter echoed round the room.

"He's a natural," Maxine said admiringly as Graham deftly removed another cushion from the floor.

Graham spotted me, waved and mouthed, "Help!"

Soon I was involved in a disco dancing competition and laying out jam tarts and jellies for the birthday tea.

Finally Graham and I got a chance to speak to each other.

"It's good to see you again," he said. "And more hands on deck too, for which I am extremely grateful."

"Oh, I'm enjoying myself," I said.

I was trying to push away the thought that this could have been my little girl's party, it could have been Peter organising the games and me who had baked the pink and white ballet girl birthday cake.

But it wasn't; it was Graham and Maxine and Rosie and Liam, a happy family, and I was on my own.

At that moment the front door opened.

"Daddy!" Rosie shrieked and ran to hurl herself at the tall man who stood smiling in the hall.

"Oh darling, well done!" Maxine called out. "How ever did you manage to get away so early?"

"The boss said he'd cover for me."

"Mark is with the Air Ambulance," Maxine said to me. "We thought he'd be on call today and have to miss Rosie's party. So we roped Graham in to help – and you too, of course!"

"Oh!" I said, eyes wide. "I thought – "

Maxine laughed. "No, no, I'm not married to Graham! He's Mark's brother."

"That's me," Graham said, grinning, "only the uncle. But I guess that I could maybe get used to all this fun and games."

"We'd give you a good reference," Maxine said, smiling.

Graham and I looked at each other.

"How do you feel about pass the parcel and ice cream with sparkles?" he asked me.

"My absolute top favourites," I said. "Both of them."

● ●

MY FAVOURITE...

My favourite book is *Pride and Prejudice* by Jane Austen. It has family relationships and love affairs going right and wrong, with a witty, strong heroine and a handsome hero.

To The Rescue!

How could Hailey persuade her grateful neighbour and bashful husband to move on after their big drama?

By Jo Styles

I'm going to hide behind the sofa," Adam said in the kitchen as the chimes of the door bell still echoed in from the hall.

I frowned. "It might not be Rose. She goes out on Saturday, I think."

"It's always Rose. I've asked her to stop. Honestly."

I knew he was protesting too much. I also knew the entire situation had left him feeling slightly bewildered.

"Stay here, out of sight, then."

In the hall, I could tell by the size of the shape behind the glass of the front door he'd guessed right. It was our neighbour. I opened the door and smiled.

"Hello, Rose."

Rose, short and round, her cheeks all aglow, wore the biggest widest smile a woman her size could handle. She thrust out her hand. "A fruit basket!"

That's not a very flattering description of yourself, Rose. I hid my smirk.

"Since I know your lovely husband doesn't want me fattening him up, I've brought apples, grapes and bananas." She cocked her head so that she could peer around me. "Is he here?"

"Er…he's in the shower," I lied.

"Should I wait?"

"No, no, I'll take his present. He'll be thrilled – thank you."

She heaved a deep sigh. "I know I ought to tone things down a bit but… well… does it sound odd to say I'm not ready yet?" She thrust the fruit basket into my hands. "I'll just be more thoughtful about my gifts from now on, if that's all right?"

"Gifts really aren't necessary."

"Oh, they are. They are." She glanced up towards the grey sheet of clouds, then nodded, as if to God himself. "Well, I'd better go. I don't want to be accused of stalking or anything, do I?"

"No, Rose." *Is stalking common in grandmothers over sixty-five?*

Assured that she had indeed gone, I carried the basket into the kitchen.

"It's all right," I said to Adam, who was hiding behind the kitchen door. "She won't give you any wet kisses this morning or try any more rib-breaking hugs."

He pretended to look relieved, but I knew he wasn't quite ready for it all to **Continued overleaf**

be over either. It's time I explained…

On Wednesday evening, he'd shattered the glass in our neighbour's front door with a hammer. He'd flicked up the latch and entered her house at the speed of a comet. Then he'd hurtled into her kitchen.

Man sees neighbour choking to death through kitchen window. That's how our local rag might have reported it, if it had got that far.

His Heimlich manoeuvre, according to Rose, had been expertly done. I'd missed all the excitement; I'd been queuing in the supermarket for tea, bread and cereal. I returned home to find a note.

Gone to the hospital with Rose. She needs a check-up. Fish for dinner can be lethal, you know.

How on earth did you thank someone for saving your life? Then again, how can you brush off your superhero act with a

He agreed that at some point with Rose.

He chewed another grape into atoms.

"I wonder what she'll turn up with tomorrow," he mused.

A car-cleaning-kit, it turned out. This time, Adam bravely answered the door himself. He received his customary bone-crushing hug with good grace and took his present, his head swelling moment by moment as Rose lavished him with praise.

Then he stared over her shoulder at the snow that had fallen overnight.

"Do you need a hand going back? That looks a bit icy, Rose. You really ought to stay inside when the weather's like this."

I witnessed his offer from the kitchen doorway. "I'm sure she'll be fine," I called. Rose really didn't need morphing into some frail old lady who'd snap like a twig at any moment.

A scream came from next door. Adam almost banged his nose on the glass

shrug? I had no idea. I just knew that neither the saviour nor the saved had moved on from all the drama.

Adam picked off a few grapes from the basket. He popped one into his mouth then, in accordance with his pact with Rose – and just about everybody else he could talk into it – he chewed very thoroughly before daring to swallow.

"Well, at least she's stopped baking you cakes and cookies," I said.

His expression turned wistful. Rose would give Mary Berry a run for her money, but cake and cookies might lead to heart attacks and furry blood vessels.

She obviously agreed with me.

"I'll be fine, pet."

"No, no, I'll just help you back to your house." He folded her hand over his arm then, in his thin sweater and the slippers his mother had bought him that looked like the feet of a big hairy bear, he guided her down our drive.

He returned half an hour later with cake crumbs all down his front.

"Her grandkids have just arrived," he said before he settled in front of the TV.

The sofa was his usual Sunday morning haunt, but today he couldn't settle. I found him upstairs a little later, peering out of our bedroom window.

"What are you doing?" I asked.

"Nothing."

In her back garden, Rose's grandchildren pushed a large ball of snow round the lawn. Rose stood by the fence, smiling away under a pink woolly hat. I narrowed my eyes at my husband. "You're not worried, are you?"

"Why would I be worried?"

"Well, it's icy out there too." His brows lifted so I went on, "Rose is a grown woman and she's very fit and healthy. Her doctor says so."

"You asked her what her doctor said?"

"Yes, I did, just in case I needed any evidence to prove her good health."

A scream came from next door. He almost banged his nose on the glass looking outside. It was one of Rose's grandchildren being pelted with a snowball, that was all. Another ball hurtled Rose's way and Adam's nails dug into the sill. It skimmed her coat by the width of a hair.

"I think I'll just go and…"

"Interfere." I stepped across his path before he could escape. "No, you won't. Why don't you go and ring your own gran and see how she's doing?"

His chest heaved. "You're right, of course. I'm over-reacting."

Still, he feigned left then darted right and charged past me. I grabbed hold of his jumper to reel him in.

"Seriously, Adam. She needs to stop saying thank you and you need to stop feeling you're responsible for her."

He gave his jumper a good solid yank and it snapped free.

"You don't know what it's like!"

I expected him to explain exactly what it was like, but he didn't. He thumped down the stairs. In the hall, he hauled on his coat and boots.

After the front door slammed, I returned to our bedroom window. He appeared in Rose's garden, received his usual hug, then was introduced to her **Continued overleaf**

Continued from previous page

grandchildren. He stood looking coy and modest. *Yes, yes, I saved her. No, no, it was nothing. Anybody would have done the same.*

He wrapped Rose's hand over his arm again in case she put a single foot wrong on the snowy path. *I'll go and fetch some bubble-wrap,* I thought. *I wonder what she'll bring you tomorrow. A bunch of red roses? That's if you ever come home.*

He did, luckily – but the following evening he was pacing the house like a caged animal.

At least, as it was Monday, work had kept him occupied and a great distance from Rose all day. Too much free time

Next door, I rang her bell. Then I rang it again.

I might have started to panic but since there wasn't a single light on in her house, I decided not to bother. Rose had clearly gone out.

I was halfway down the drive when a taxi came swinging into the kerb. Rose climbed out onto the pavement.

"Hello, Hailey!" She waved at me with one thick mitten.

"Hello, Rose."

It was then I noticed movement behind our hedge. *Oh for God's sake, Adam. Enough is enough.*

"You'll never guess where I've been." Rose beamed up at me. "I've been to the church hall to learn first-aid. You will tell

I might have started to panic but I noticed no lights were on in her house

over the weekend definitely hadn't helped anybody move on.

Minutes ticked by as he wandered from kitchen to lounge.

"It's nearly nine and she hasn't been round. Do you think she's all right?"

"You don't think she's sick of the sight of you, do you?"

"Don't be silly. She loves me. I think I'll go round. She might have had another accident or something."

"I wish you'd stop thinking that way. I'll go round instead – but not because I think she's hurt. I need a word with her."

"What kind of a word?"

Maybe he ought to have guessed what kind by now?

"You stay here and don't move an inch until I get back. All right?"

Adam, won't you?" Her expression grew grave. "Actually I did want a word with you about him. I think things are getting a little… strained now. I usually play with my grandchildren, you see. We love a good old snowball fight but he wouldn't let me move an inch yesterday afternoon.

"Anyway, tell him I can set a bone now. I even know what to do if I have a fall or think I've had a stroke. God forbid. I'll always be grateful for what he did for me, but I think it's time we both realised I can look after myself. In fact, I can even look after other people now as well. Isn't that wonderful?"

I glanced to the hedge where I was sure Adam still lurked.

"I'll tell him," I said.

"He is lovely."

"Of course he is. He knows that."

"Well, I'd better go." Rose tiptoed around the patches of ice on the Tarmac and disappeared inside.

I hurried back up my own drive, not surprised at all to find Adam wasn't behind the hedge any more. He'd done a runner back into the house.

Inside, he acted all innocent as if he hadn't eavesdropped at all

"Is she all right?" he asked.

"Yes, she's fine." I told him the rest and he nodded his way through it as if every word was fresh.

"Yes, I can see her point," he said sagely. "It was a very good idea, her going to learn first-aid. It's a very good way of feeling you're back in control. I'm sure she'll be fine on her own now. I have no need to worry."

I sat down in his lap and he wrapped his arms about me. "That's right, love, *you have nothing to fret about.*" I emphasised every word.

He gave a throaty cough in reply. Then he wheezed like a radiator venting air. I shot to my feet and stood wide-eyed as he leaned over and thumped at his chest. "Are you all right? Oh my God!"

I think it was when he started to sound like a cat trying to hack up a fur ball and tried to disguise a snigger that I guessed what a faker he was.

"Oh Adam, that's not funny. I thought you were really choking to death."

He wore a very grave expression then.

"You didn't know what to do, did you? I *do* have something to worry about. I mean, I know first-aid. Rose is becoming an expert but…" He frowned at me. "In an emergency what use are you, Hailey?"

He did have a point, didn't he? It's no good agreeing it's a good idea to know first-aid when you don't know a plaster from a splint yourself.

"You're right. I do need to learn."

He tapped at his lips. "I need a big kiss now as a thank you for guiding your way."

"Well, I would," I replied with a smirk, "but I'm off next door to ask Rose which class she's going to. I think I'll join her."

"So, no kiss then?" My hero looked so utterly crushed.

"You'll have to wait ten minutes." I grinned. "But don't worry Adam, I promise I will come back and rescue you."

• •

MY FAVOURITE…

A real feel-good read when you need one is *The House at Ladywell* by Nicola Slade. Gentle and multi-layered, it has mystery, history, romance and a touch of magic.

First Day

Thandi finds that there is so much to learn – but the greatest lesson of all is how to be kind…

By Jenny Robson

T handi Dlamini was six-and-a-half when she learned the terrible truth about her mother.

It was Thandi's very first day at proper big school and she was learning so many new things. For a start, she learned that she was a brave little girl. That's what her pretty teacher, Miss Moeti, said.

"You are such a brave little girl, Thandi! Well done!"

It was time for the mothers to leave so lessons could begin. Some children cried. Some clung to their mothers' skirts. Some even threw tantrums. But not Thandi.

No, she just gave her mother a hug, then waved goodbye with a big smile. Thandi was so excited to be at proper big school. She wanted to learn all the things her clever big sister Olona could do. Like writing the whole alphabet in order! Like counting to twenty without stopping once.

Thandi learned a good deal that very first morning. She found out how to hold her pencil properly, the way Olona did. She learned that when Miss Moeti spoke, you had to answer "Yes, Ma'am" or "No, Ma'am" or "I don't know, Ma'am". And if you wanted to go to the bathroom, you had to put your hand up first and say, "Please may I be excused, Ma'am?"

She also learned that you weren't allowed to take your shoes and socks off when your feet felt hot and itchy.

Thandi also learned that her seat was the one beside a girl called Victoria. And that when the huge boy from Grade Seven rang the bell, it meant break-time had come. And break-time meant that you could take your food outside and talk to your new friends.

It was at break-time that Thandi finally learned the truth about her mother.

S he was sitting on the grass with Victoria and another Grade One girl called Shalani. The sun was shining down. Children were rushing all around them, kicking balls or playing clapping games or jumping rope.

Thandi was enjoying the pineapple jam sandwich her mother had packed. Pineapple jam was her favourite.

That's when Shalani said the most terrible thing.

"Why is your mother so ugly, Thandi?"

"Yes," Victoria chimed in. "I thought she was a monster. Like in a movie. I got so scared, I nearly screamed!"

Thandi did not walk away, mostly because she couldn't move. She was numb with shock. Was it true? Was her mother really ugly?

Thandi tried to picture her mother's face, but all she could remember was her mother's arms wrapped around her when she was sad, and her mother's gentle

voice when Thandi fell and hurt herself. And her mother's sweet smell when she tucked Thandi under her duvet at night. And her mother's lovely smile when she came to wake Thandi up each morning with sweet tea.

After break-time, Thandi struggled to learn. She found it hard to concentrate on what Miss Moeti was telling them. Her head was buzzing – as if it were full of angry bees. Did all the other children also think her mother was ugly? Did Miss Moeti?

"Thandi? Can you tell us the answer?" The teacher was talking to her, but Thandi hadn't even heard the question!

"I don't know, Ma'am," she mumbled. Victoria giggled beside her.

For the last lesson, the children had to draw a picture. Thandi bent over her **Continued overleaf**

Continued from previous page

white paper and drew carefully.

"What are you drawing, dear?" Miss Moeti asked.

"I'm drawing you, Ma'am," said Thandi. "You are the most beautiful lady I have ever seen."

Miss Moeti smiled. "Thank you, Thandi, but remember, beauty is only skin deep. The important thing is being beautiful inside. Being kind and gentle and treating other people well – that's what makes someone really beautiful."

Thandi nodded, but when she looked up at Miss Moeti's lovely smile, she thought: *I wish my mother was pretty like my teacher. Then Victoria and Shalani wouldn't say mean things.*

half-closed as if she were about to fall asleep. And a piece of Mama's nose seemed to be missing – as if some rat had nibbled it. Worse still, the skin around Mama's cheek was twisted up and pulled askew. It had a shiny look, like a black plastic rubbish-bag.

How had she had never noticed before? Thandi wondered. Had Mama always looked this way?

Thandi's mother stopped stirring the pot. "What is it? Why are you staring, sweetheart?"

Thandi's mother smiled. And that was the worst moment! Suddenly Thandi realized just how awful her mother's smile was. Just how frightening! Half her mouth pulled downwards under the

How had she never noticed before? Had Mama always looked that way?

The huge boy from Grade Seven rang the golden bell again for home-time. Olona came to fetch Thandi home.

"So how was your first day, little sis?" asked Olona.

"It was fine," Thandi lied. But what else could she say?

"What new things did you learn?"

Thandi didn't even try to answer.

That evening, while her mother chopped the vegetables, Thandi sat in the kitchen and stared at her mother's face, and she began to see what Victoria and Shalani meant.

Yes, her mother's face was different from the faces of the other mothers who had stood at the classroom door that morning.

One of Mama's eyes was scary and

plastic-bin-bag skin and too many teeth showed. Victoria was right – it was the smile of a monster!

Thandi couldn't help herself. The words came rushing out.

"Why are you so ugly, Mama? My friends say you are so ugly. Why can't you be pretty like Miss Moeti?"

Just then, Thandi's clever big sister Olona walked in.

And everything turned bad and horrible. Thandi's mother sat down at the table, crying, so big tears dropped from her half-closed eye and ran down her shiny bin-bag cheek. At the same time Olona was screaming.

"How dare you say such cruel things, Thandi? Is that what you learned at school today – how to be cruel and nasty?"

Thandi had never seen her sister so angry. She ran out into the yard and hid behind some bricks. She was crying now, too. Today was supposed to be the best, most exciting day of her life, but instead it was turning awful!

Olona found her there behind the bricks. Olona had stopped being angry. Instead she spoke quietly.

"Thandi, I'm going to tell you about what happened long ago when you were just two. And then you will understand."

It had been a Saturday morning, Olona said. They were in a taxi, all three of them, going off to Johannesburg to buy some warm winter clothes.

"You were so excited," said Olona. "You kept saying, 'Me want pink jacket, Mama. Me want pink jacket with fluff on.' And Mama was laughing. You know how lovely Mama's laugh sounds. And she said, 'We will find a pink fluffy jacket if we have to try every shop in Johannesburg! I promise!' And that moment was when our taxi crashed…"

It wasn't a bad accident, so Olona said. The passengers were able to climb out quickly and get onto the pavement. All except Thandi. Two-year-old Thandi was stuck, wedged between two seats that had buckled. And all except Mama.

"Mama wouldn't get out, even with the driver screaming at her to leave it until the police and paramedics arrived," Olona continued. "But no! Mama wouldn't leave you. She was trying to get you free, ripping at the seats, trying to pull them

apart… then the fire started, just a small one at first. I was screaming so much, my head felt like it would burst. But even when the fire spread across the seats, still Mama wouldn't leave you. She wrapped her scarf around you to protect you from the flames.

"Yes, Thandi, Mama stayed right there, until she managed to pull you free. They took Mama straight to hospital because her face was so badly burned. Terrible! There were strips of charred skin hanging from her cheeks. I nearly went crazy, seeing her like that!"

Mama had been in hospital a long time, Olona said. The doctors tried to do skin grafts, tried to repair and re-construct, but the damage was mostly too deep.

"That's why Mama's face looks like that, Thandi. Because she rescued you. Because she wouldn't leave you. Do you understand?"

Thandi nodded. Yes, she understood. After all, she was a big girl now, going to proper school.

Thandi ran back into the kitchen and flung her arms around her mother.

"You are the most beautiful mother in the world," she said. "And you are the bravest person in the whole world too!"

Tomorrow at break, Thandi decided, that's exactly what she would tell her new friends Victoria and Shalani.

MY FAVOURITE…

I read the book _We, The Living_ by Ayn Rand at the age of 16 and I remember hoping that one day I might touch people's lives in the way she had touched mine.

Now You
See It...

Having reluctantly donned her new glasses, Rose discovers she simply needs to change her focus

By Paula Williams

I t's only vanity, you know," Rose could hear Deirdre, her daughter-in-law saying. "That's the reason your mother won't wear her glasses. Sheer vanity. At her age, it's so dangerous. Next time she could fall and break her hip. Then where would we be?"

Rose thought she'd most likely be parked on a trolley in a corridor somewhere outside A&E, but Deirdre would be at work, considering how the wheels of industry would probably stop turning if Deirdre was absent from her desk for more than half an hour.

And why was she talking as if Rose wasn't in the room? Did she think tripping over the coffee table and spraining her wrist had somehow rendered her deaf at the same time, not to mention doolally?

Deirdre had never liked her. And it was all Rose's fault – for telling her the very first time they met that her son, Malcolm, didn't like Brussels sprouts.

"He'll like *my* sprouts," Deirdre had said firmly and that was that. The pattern of their relationship was set.

And now she was insisting that

Malcolm take Rose to see an optician immediately to see about getting new glasses. There was no point in Rose telling Deirdre she didn't want new glasses. As for saying that she'd probably lose them – she'd left her last pair on a coach after a day trip to Bognor Regis – as a strategy that was fatally flawed. Deirdre would have her in a home for the bewildered before you could say demented!

No, Rose didn't want – or need – new glasses. She managed perfectly well without them. But once Deirdre had decided on a course of action, resistance was as futile as Canute holding back the tide – or Malcolm finding the courage to say he really didn't like sprouts.

T here you are, Mum," Malcolm said a week later when he handed her the new glasses. "That's a lot better, isn't it?"

"They're fine, thank you." Rose's voice was subdued. "And it was very kind of you to collect them, but I could have done it myself. I'm still capable of getting on a bus to the town centre, you know."

"Of course you are," he said, a shade too heartily for Rose's liking. As if he was trying to convince himself of that fact.

Rose waited until he'd gone before she took a second look in the mirror. It was even worse than the first one.

Her wrinkles, which she'd always thought weren't too bad, considering, were so deep you could plant potatoes in them. She had wrinkles on her wrinkles while the puckering around the mouth made the bottom half of her face look like a carelessly drawn drawstring bag. As for the rest of her face, it was as crumpled and rumpled as a teenager's unmade bed.

Was Deirdre right after all? Was she vain? Because, if so, she had nothing to be vain about. She was as old and faded as the sitting room wallpaper, which until now she'd quite liked.

Her depression deepened as she looked around the room. Yes, she could indeed see the coffee table quite clearly now so she wasn't about to fall over it again – but she could also see the watermarks and coffee stains on it.

She'd always liked this room, but why hadn't she seen it for what it really was? Drab, dreary and past its sell by date. Just like her.

As for Frank, she gave a quiet murmur of despair as she thought of the Cary Grant lookalike who'd recently moved into the flat below hers. The man who'd set the heart of every woman in the place, including her own, into a bit of a doodah.
Continued overleaf

Continued from previous page

How had she ever thought she was in with a chance? Just because he'd smiled at her in what she'd thought was a special way. He'd probably been grimacing, only she'd been too short-sighted to see it.

"Glad to see you've got some new glasses at last," her friend Audrey from across the landing remarked later that morning.

"They show up every line and wrinkle," Rose said gloomily.

"Oh, you shouldn't worry about them," Audrey said. "Life's too short. I hope when I get to your age I won't waste it worrying about a few wrinkles."

Rose bristled. Audrey was four years younger than Rose and never passed up an opportunity to rub it in.

After Audrey left, to "glam herself up" as she put it, in preparation for the afternoon's quiz in the Community Room, Rose took her glasses off and her world returned to normal.

Except, of course, there was no normal. Now she knew about the wrinkles and water stains, there was no going back.

She walked across to the window and looked out. It was not something she did very often as the only things she could see from her window were rooftops and chimney pots. But now, with her new glasses on, she realised that in fact there were birds nesting in the eaves of the house opposite, while beyond that she could see the park, where an avenue of horse chestnut trees was coming into glorious, exuberant flower.

Maybe this afternoon instead of going to the quiz, which wasn't really her thing, she'd take a walk to the park to see them close up. She was always fond of horse chestnuts in spring. They reminded her of young Victorian ladies shaking out their crinolines.

Like the rose-coloured glasses in the saying, Rose's new glasses really did make her see the world differently – and not all of it for the worse. Who cared about a few wrinkles when you could watch a pair of birds busy building a nest?

She'd also seen – although, of course, she was too kind to comment – that there were hairs growing out of the mole on Audrey's chin.

And when Frank came by later that day, she noticed that he had as many wrinkles as she did – although he still had that Cary Grant smile which made her heart sing.

Frank, it appeared, knew about birds and he'd come over to identify the ones nesting in the eaves. Maybe later, she'd suggest a stroll to the park, to watch the horse chestnuts shake out their crinolines.

After that, who knows?

MY FAVOURITE...

I've always loved the phrase "rose-coloured glasses", which inspired this story. I had the first line (and disapproving Deirdre) before I'd even decided how the story would end!

Mini Christmas Eton Mess

Ingredients
(Makes 8 small or 4 regular)

- ◆ **150g strawberries, quartered**
- ◆ **100g pomegranate seeds**
- ◆ **100g seedless red grapes, chopped**
- ◆ **2tbsp brandy**
- ◆ **400ml double cream**
- ◆ **2 meringue shells, lightly crushed**
- ◆ **3tbsp strawberry syrup**
- ◆ **Mint sprigs, to garnish**

1 Put the strawberries, pomegranate and grapes into a bowl with the brandy and stir well. Share between 8 mini or 4 regular serving glasses, reserving a little for decoration.

2 Whip the cream in a chilled bowl until thick, then partially stir through the crushed meringues and strawberry syrup. Spoon the mixture into the glasses.

3 Finish off the desserts with the reserved fruit. Keep covered and chilled. When ready to serve, decorate with mint sprigs.

RECIPE AND FOOD STYLING: SUE ASHWORTH PHOTOGRAPHY: JONATHAN SHORT

The
Thrill
Of The
Chase

Ermina's keen mind is
needed to find a fair lady...

By Hayley Johnson-Mack

S ince childhood, Ermina La Vasse
had considered Guy Bonell her
particular property. So she
would not view his return to her home
– after a year's absence – in the company
of a pretty young woman as anything
other than a threat.

Add to that the fact that Avice Galliol
was also a fragile flutterbug whom Guy
seemed to find attractive, and Ermina and
she were not destined to be friends.

"Why are these people here?" she
demanded of her father.

Baldwin La Vasse smiled indulgently
at her through his beard.

"I told you, love, for hunting. In reality,
of course, Lord Galliol seeks to win back
King Henry's favour after siding with his
queen and princes in the late rebellion.

"He knows I have the king's ear, so he
comes to convince me – and therefore,
Henry – of his loyalty."

Ermina flushed as he added, "Guy
Bonell is looking fit. Knighthood obviously
agrees with him."

She didn't reply, merely sank into a
reluctant curtsey as the young man
approached to make his obeisance.
Baldwin grasped his hand.

"Glad to see you, Guy. I am eager to
hear all your news."

"As I am to share it, my lord." Guy's
gaze rested on the coltish figure by his

side. "Good morrow, Lady Ermina. I trust that you are well."

"Oh, get off your high horse," Ermina scoffed. "You've only just won your spurs, you know."

Laughing, Baldwin waved a hand toward the long stone hall at the heart of his manor.

"Come within, sir, to my lady wife. You'll not get any special treatment here."

Having caught the wounded look on Guy's face, Ermina watched his broad, handsome form climb the steps alongside her father, wishing she had curbed her impulsive tongue.

Continued overleaf

She was still wishing it some time later when she was forced to watch Guy share a trencher with the Lady Avice, who seemed so helpless that he had to carve her food and pass her each sliver.

Ermina couldn't believe that winning his spurs would change Guy so much that he'd actually enjoy this maiden's giggles, but when she broached the matter with her mother, Lady Blanche was unsurprised.

"Guy is a man full grown, Ermina, and no longer the boy you could match on horseback and fish with. Some men like a lady to be more subtle – in appearance at least."

who'd sided against him. Lord Galliol was one of those striving to win back his favour; it was only natural he should take hospitality from Henry's trusted kinsman, and only Ermina's fancy that his daughter had some other reason for stopping here.

"'Tis a fine night."

Ermina felt an unaccustomed shyness as Guy came to stand beside her.

"I thought you would be dancing," she murmured, glancing at him.

"You know I have two left feet," he replied, reaching for her hand, and just like that, the strain between them fell away… only to return at the sound of light footsteps.

"I worry that Father's enemies may seek to get revenge on him through me"

"She is very pretty," Ermina conceded. Lady Blanche smiled.

"So are you, in your own special way."

Ermina smiled back, but distractedly, and when the fiddlers' tunes grew livelier to encourage the guests to dance, excused herself. She was hoping Guy would follow, as he had done in the past.

The stars were out in force tonight. From her favourite sheltered niche on the south wall, Ermina lost herself in their sparkling depths.

Though her family's loyalty to the crown meant they'd been protected from the plots of Queen Eleanor and her sons against King Henry in the recent rebellion, Ermina knew what had occurred. A triumphant King Henry forgave his sons, but that benevolence had not extended to his estranged queen or certain nobles

Both turned to see Lady Avice.

"Sir Guy," she said, her voice surprisingly strong for one so delicate. "I wonder if I might speak with you."

"Of course," Guy said. "You may speak freely in front of Ermina; I would trust her with my life. What is it that troubles you?"

"I believe that my father and I may be in danger. Papa is an influential man. Both sides of the recent struggle wanted his support, and there are rebels who now wish him ill for turning back to the King.

"I have lately felt we were being watched, and followed, and I worry that Father's enemies may seek to get revenge on him through me."

"Have you discussed this with him?"

"I did try. But Father doesn't entertain what he calls my superstitious fancies."

"It was a difficult war," said Guy soothingly. "It has left us all checking

shadows. But it would be a brave man who sought to take on the might of Lord Galliol. Remain vigilant, my lady, and I am sure all will be well."

Avice sighed.

"Yes, no doubt you are right, and I worry too much."

With his warmth still lingering in her palm, Ermina found herself feeling sorry for the girl. If she was hoping to secure Guy's aid in some kind of scheme, she'd clearly failed. Then she caught sight of the self-satisfied expression on Avice's face, and her sympathy disappeared.

As presaged by the previous night's stars, the new day dawned bright, perfect weather for the planned hunt in Baldwin's forest.

With her knight at her side, Ermina was in her element as the party of riders followed dogs through the trees in search of deer. The scent was strong and before long, horse and hound gave chase.

Hard on their quarry's heels, Ermina was surprised to see the Lady Avice veering off in another direction, away from the pack. Was she trying to head the

Continued overleaf

Continued from previous page

quarry off from the side? Shrugging, Ermina faced front again. This was one game the girl wasn't going to win.

In the triumphant aftermath, no one noticed at first that Avice was missing. Then her riderless horse appearing in the meadow caused the guards on the gate to shout to those below, and Galliol to round on Baldwin.

"My lord seems upset," Ermina observed to Guy, eyes narrowed.

believing you or she could be in danger," Guy ventured.

Galliol looked aghast.

"She said as much to me and I scorned the idea. By God, Baldwin, there may be darker forces at work. We must find her!"

Baldwin, agreeing, hurried off to arrange a wider search while Galliol plunged into the trees, shouting his daughter's name. Ermina remained in the clearing, examining the hoofmarks on the forest floor.

"Come, Ermina," Guy said anxiously.

"You are not so blinded by envy that you would have us abandon the search?"

"Of course," he muttered. "His daughter's horse has returned alone. That means something's happened to her."

"Nonsense," Ermina declared. And stepping up to her Papa, she told how she'd seen Avice veer off the hunters' path. Baldwin seemed relieved.

"She's no doubt lost her way or taken a tumble somewhere. We'll head back out and help her home."

Ermina joined the party returning to the woods, directing them to where she'd seen my lady leave the chase. Fanning out, they began to search.

Before long a clearing in the beechwood with broken branches showed where Avice had been unhorsed. But of the lady herself, there was no sign. Baldwin tried to reassure her fretful father that she couldn't be far.

"Then why does she not answer?" Galliol demanded.

"My lady spoke of threats, lord, of

"I shall escort you safely home."

She eased herself out of his arms.

"There's no need; I am not in danger. Guy, look, do not those branches seem too precisely snapped to have been broken by someone falling from their horse? And these hoofmarks…"

"What are you trying to say, Ermina?"

"This whole thing…" Ermina gestured round the glade. "It's all too neat."

Guy frowned.

"Avice was right; she was in danger, and now someone has taken her."

Ermina shook her head.

"There is something strange at work here, but I am sure it is not abduction. My lady is too good a rider to have been thrown from her horse. Nay, she's been playing us since she arrived. This must be part of the same silly game…"

Guy stared at her.

"Surely you cannot be so blinded by envy of a pretty young maid that you'd have us abandon the search for her?"

"Of course not," Ermina snapped. "But trust me, something is amiss here."

"If that is true," said Guy, "then I need to know that you are somewhere safe. Please, Ermina, go home."

Guy might think that Ermina's doubt stemmed from jealousy but she knew better. Now all she had to do was prove it.

Galliol's groom showed a flattering deference when she paid him a visit but his information did naught to aid her mission – though he did refuse to believe Avice had been unhorsed.

"It's never happened before. I've had the care of her since she took her first ride."

"Perhaps she got carried away in the excitement of the chase," Ermina said.

"Perhaps. But she's no stranger to the hunt – and as I say, 't'ain't never happened before."

Ermina thanked him, convinced that this proved Avice did not fall from her horse by accident, if at all. To be certain, she sought out Avice's maid in the hopes that she could shed more light on the situation. Little Mylla didn't disappoint.

"It's so dreadful," she wailed. "I do hope nothing's happened to her."

"Did she mention anything about being afraid, or nervous?" Ermina asked.

"Afraid? No, mistress. Not afraid."

"What, then?"

"Well, excited." Lashes lowered, Mylla added, "She's in love."

Ermina frowned.

"Really? Who's the lucky man?"

"She never said," the maid admitted.

"Then how can you say she's in love?"

Mylla's smile was conspiratorial.

"A woman knows these things."

As the hunt for Avice continued, whispered rumours of vengeful rebels grew. Frowning, Ermina quickened her step as she hurried out of the gates. Now, it wasn't just to prove herself correct that she had to find my lady.

When she had walked length and breadth of manor and meadowland and still found naught, Ermina's confidence began to waver. Mayhap Guy was right, and she had been influenced by envy.

She was heading home, disconsolate, when the sudden flight of roosting birds made her start. She watched them whirl upon the air, then turned toward the barn **Continued overleaf**

from which they'd burst. It was used only by forest creatures nowadays. So what had disturbed the starlings?

Cautiously, she picked her way towards it. Inside, all was still, dancing dust motes embracing cracks of sunlight in peaceful silence. Yet Ermina could feel a prickling in her spine, as though she were not alone.

Guy's worries ringing in her ears, she began to back towards the door. It was only when she had the solid frame in her hand that she noticed the fresh scuff marks in the dust on the boards beside the loft ladder.

Guy saved Ermina the trouble of looking for him as he rode into the bailey at the same moment she arrived there. She ran to him, agitated.

"I need you to come with me."

He snatched at the reins to hold the horse steady.

"To where, exactly?"

"The old weaver's shed. I think I've found something."

When Ermina re-entered the barn, all was as tranquil as before, and she felt a momentary doubt. But when she glanced toward Guy, he had a finger to his lips and was gesturing for her to follow behind him to the foot of the stepladder.

"We know you are up there, my lady," he called, keeping Ermina tucked behind him. "It is time to come out."

There was a pause, then a rustling and a moment later, Avice's face came into view. Guy sighed in relief.

"Thank goodness you are safe, lady. We have all been looking for you."

"I am sorry for that," she said softly. "But it was unavoidable."

Guy frowned.

"What do you mean?"

"I believe I know," Ermina murmured. "What is a little inconvenience in the pursuit of love, eh, my lady? For that is why all this has been done, is it not?"

There was defiance in the lovely face now but also shame as Avice admitted, "Aye, for love – for a life with one my father would prevent me from marrying. He is a firm supporter of Queen Eleanor, you see, and totally against the king.

"He and Father quarrelled, and I was forbidden to see him. We came up with this plan in a secret meeting as soon as I learned we were to go hunting in Baldwin

La Vasse's fabled woods. I would appear to be lost or abducted, then hide away until dark, when my love would come for me. Not a brilliant plan, granted, but we thought it would suffice." She turned curious eyes on Ermina. "How did you find me out?"

Ermina shrugged.

"The whole thing was too contrived, like the staging of a mummer's play, with yourself the proverbial damsel in distress."

Avice laughed. "Thank Heaven I need not earn my bread by those means, then! Is there no chance you will keep my secret until nightfall?"

Guy shook his head.

"Men are combing the forest for you,

"Endeavour deserves reward."

"You have grown wiser in my absence," Guy observed. "If not for you, we'd still be searching for abductors."

Ermina shrugged. "Sometimes, the truth is simpler than political intrigue."

"Love is a powerful thing," he agreed quietly. "One that can make folk act foolish."

Ermina swallowed.

"If you mean me, I am aware that I'm impetuous and not at all subtle. But I am what I am and I'm not sure I can change."

"Good, I am glad, for I wouldn't want you any other way."

There was something in Guy's voice that set Ermina's heart thudding.

Hearing a familiar tread behind her, she knew she had been waiting for it

and one is in despair for what might have befallen his beloved child. Come down, now, lady," he said in a softer tone, "and give your father a chance to grant you happiness. He may surprise you."

Feeling restive, Ermina sought out her favourite south wall spot. From this vantage point, she was able to witness the return of Avice to the hall, and the subsequent recall of the searchers.

She wondered whether my lady would be able to appease her father and get her man. She found herself hoping she would. When she heard a familiar tread behind her, she knew she'd been waiting for it.

"Lady Avice may yet win the day," Guy reported, resting elbows on the parapet. "Galliol is so relieved to have her back unharmed, he is apt to agree to anything."

"I am glad for it," said Ermina sincerely.

"Say you love me, Ermina, and you'll still have me as your man."

Ermina pretended to consider, smiling. With a curse, Guy pulled her into his arms.

"I admit I was mistaken in Avice, but I shall be happy to let you instruct me in the finer points of women's characters from now on."

"Indeed?" Ermina's smile widened. "Then let us begin with the best way to kiss your future wife."

Guy laughed and tilted her chin to meet his mouth…

MY FAVOURITE…

Susanna Kearsley's _The Shadowy Horses_ is my favourite book. A fantastical, romantic, atmospheric Scottish tale with engaging characters. Unputdownable.

Wonder Woman

Yes, that's exactly what Lynn had to become in order to win round Craig's reluctant young daughter...

by Mhairi Grant

H ave you ever killed anyone?" It was not what I expected to be asked by a seven-year old. I glanced at my boyfriend, Caitlin's father.

"I don't think so... although I almost poisoned someone with my Irish stew."

"Huh," she said and stalked off.

I turned to Craig and said, "Have I come after a long line of black widows after you for your money or something?"

"Nope, I just happen to have a daughter who would give Attilla the Hun a good run for his money."

Two minutes later Caitlin came back, demonstrated a few Kung Fu-style kicks, and then, hands on hips, asked, "Do you do any martial arts then?"

Martial arts? Me? Was she kidding? As a child, I was into pink and My Little Pony. The closest I ever got to violence was when I scratched my big sister for stealing my pony.

"Er... no."

"Caitlin goes to Taekwondo classes," said Craig – the proud parent.

I almost blurted out, *So? I went to ballet classes!* But I bit my tongue. I was trying hard to appear the mature, sensible and child-orientated adult who could take tantrums, teething problems and a hostile child in her stride.

Caitlin started up her Kung Fu or Teecando thing again, killing off imaginary opponents. She kicked and punched her way round the room until she stopped with her foot about an inch away from my face.

Craig beamed and I gave a *bless-her* smile. I was beginning to see why it had taken Craig months to introduce me to his daughter, especially, when I saw the steely look in her eye. I eyed her back.

To this day, I don't know what came over me, but the Batman theme popped into my head. I used to be Robin to my nephew's Batman and we used to play endlessly.

I struck a kick-ass pose and said in my Batman voice, "We both looked into the abyss – the only difference is, you blinked."

Caitlin did more than blink, her mouth fell open!

I then demonstrated a few moves of my own... WHAM! POW! "*Batman... Batman... Batman...*" I sang.

I could tell Caitlin was impressed.

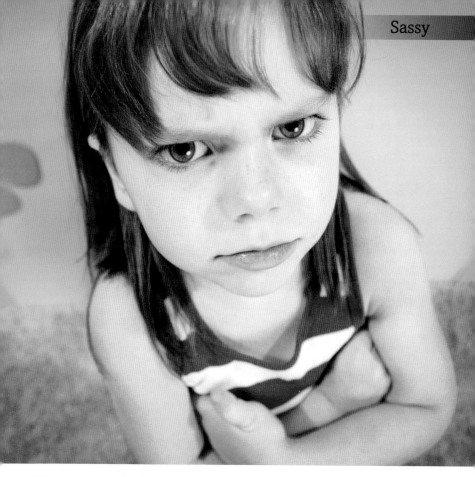

Then my arm caught a lamp and it crashed to the floor.

Craig smothered his face in a cushion and started to laugh. Chastened, I picked up the lamp and apologised.

Then I looked at a wide-eyed Caitlin.

"Batman?" she said in a disbelieving voice. "*Batman?*"

Then she turned in disgust and stomped off to her bedroom. I slumped down on the settee next to Craig.

"That went well. Don't you think?"

But he couldn't answer. He was still laughing. If Caitlin had laughed, it could have broken the ice and made things easier for Craig as well. He only saw his daughter at weekends, as the rest of the week Caitlin stayed with her mother, and I didn't want to ruin their precious quality time together.

She'll come around, Lynn," he told me later. "You're the first woman I've ever introduced her to, so give her time and I'm sure she'll love you like I do."

Craig put a positive spin on everything. That's what I loved about him. His wife had left him for her childhood sweetheart when he'd come back on the scene. Craig had been devastated but not bitter, and I've never heard him say a bad word **Continued overleaf** about her – or anyone, for that matter.

"It must have been meant," he'd said recently, "because if we hadn't divorced I wouldn't have met you."

Although early days, I knew we had a future together and I knew that Caitlin was part of that future. So, I was determined to be her friend.

Caitlin had other ideas. She seemed barely able to even talk to me. Until one day, out of the blue, she asked, "What's the worst thing that's ever happened to you?"

I censored my thoughts trying to think of something suitable for tender ears.

"Nothing. I didn't report it. He was just having a bad day and thought my leg was part of the bike. I love dogs, you see. I have one of my own."

Caitlin had apparently lost interest and sauntered off, ignoring me completely. Nevertheless, that was the longest conversation I had with her.

She really does like you," said Craig. "But she's finding it difficult to share her time with me."

"She won't even let me plait her hair," I murmured, "and it's the one thing I'm really good at. I know lots of different styles. Is she open to bribery?"

"Nope – 'fraid not. Her stepfather tried

She gave a blood-curdling yell and struck, but I'd seen the film, I knew the moves

Meanwhile Caitlin fought her way through an army of baddies.

"I was bitten by a Rottweiler once," I said eventually.

That stopped her killing spree.

"A Rottweiler? Really?"

"Yep. I was on a squeaky bike and the dog ran out and grabbed the wheel. I stopped and he bit my leg."

"Did you cry?"

"No, of course I didn't cry," I said indignantly. "But it did hurt."

"Have you got a scar?"

Yep," I replied, rolling up my jeans leg to show her.

Caitlin peered at the teeny weeny white line on my leg. Only one tooth had penetrated.

"Is that all?' she said, obviously unimpressed. "What happened to the dog?'

that approach. It got him nowhere."

"He's been her stepfather for two years. Please, tell me she speaks to him!"

"After a fashion…"

At the look on my face he started to laugh. I hit him with a cushion. It was all very well to kid me on, but Caitlin and me had some serious bonding to do.

Craig helped all he could, involving the three of us in various projects, and Caitlin went along with it. But that's all she did – went along with it. It called for a change in strategy. But what?

Strange how the subconscious works. I don't normally go and see action-packed hero films, but *Wonder Woman* was different. For a start, she was female. I went with a friend and I came out of that film, feeling empowered. I was a woman with attitude. The colour pink and My Little Pony were no longer part of my psyche. I was into girl power.

"Bring it on, Caitlin," I murmured, flexing my muscles.

The very next day, I got my chance. For the first time, Craig brought Caitlin to my house. She entered as if it was booby-trapped.

"There are no lurking baddies here," I said, "only super heroes."

"Batman," she scoffed, giving me a smile that clearly said *saddo!*

"No, only Diana, Princess of the Amazons and the daughter of Zeus lives here!"

"Who?"

"Wonder Woman."

Caitlin's eyes lit up. She bounced on the balls of her feet and demonstrated some

of her Teecando moves. I copied her. We circled the kitchen table. I daren't look at Craig in case he was smirking. This was serious. This was a battle – for her heart.

Caitlin let out a blood-curdling yell and struck. I feinted. I'd seen the film, I knew the moves. I must say, Caitlin was fast. But I was fit. We parried each other's blows. Caitlin jumped on a chair, let out another blood-curdling yell, ready to leap.

WOOF!

Caitlin froze.

I stopped and looked at my dog. He'd been in the garden but was now standing in the kitchen doorway staring at Caitlin.

"Is he a wolf?" she whispered.

"No, he's a German Shepherd and he's called Sabre."

He was a very big and hairy German Shepherd and he was also a big softy.

Will he attack?" Caitlin asked. She sounded almost nervous – or was she simply impressed?

"Only if you try to kill me." I turned to my dog. "Stand down, Sabre."

My dog sat down and looked at me with his big, molten eyes. I signalled to him to come. He wagged his tail. Caitlin slowly climbed off the chair.

"Come and say hello to him."

"Is he a guard dog?"

I looked at Craig and he smiled. He always thought that Caitlin would love Sabre. He hunkered down and scratched Sabre's ears.

Still, Caitlin hung back.

"Yes, he is but he is also a member of this household and I love him dearly." I turned to my dog. "Go and say hello to Caitlin, Sabre."

My lovely dog went up to her and sniffed her face before giving it a lick. She grinned and then put her arms round Sabre's neck.

Then she turned to me and said, "Can we take him for a walk, Lynn? Please."

"Of course we can."

It was much later after the walk and non-stop chatter that Caitlin confided, "I thought your dog was a pink poodle!"

"Heaven forbid – a pink poodle! Would Wonder Woman have a pink poodle?"

Then we all laughed.

Wonder Woman and Sabre. Who would have thought it?

● ●

MY FAVOURITE...

The Snow Child by Eowyn Ivey is a tale of a wild child in an Alaskan wilderness. It's pure enchantment!

Braver Than Brave

A pair of bright pink earmuffs and a nervous puppy was all it took for little Amelia to find her own courage

By Jan Snook

Everyone in the family liked fireworks. Everyone, that was, except five-year-old Amelia, who was currently shaking her head stubbornly and glaring at them all with narrowed eyes. Caroline looked at her youngest granddaughter in consternation.

"But bonfire night is such fun! We all get dressed in our warmest clothes, with hats and scarves and gloves and boots and coats, and we go out in the dark and join the procession to the field where the fireworks are. And lots of people carry flaming torches…"

Amelia was looking up at Caroline, her eyes as big as lollipops, and beginning to nod reluctantly.

"And then they light the bonfire, and there's a funny guy on the top. There are sparklers and a roaring fire, and everyone who was cold is suddenly lovely and warm. And if you get hungry there are stalls selling jacket potatoes, and sausages and hot chocolate."

"Hot chocolate?" a little voice echoed.

"Yes, hot chocolate! We all have a lovely time," Caroline said coaxingly.

Amelia was still nodding mutely, but her hands had fluttered towards her face, and her bottom lip had started to wobble.

"Then there are the fireworks," Caroline continued enthusiastically, "red and gold and silver and blue and green… great big sunbursts of colour in the sky like gigantic glittery dandelion clocks. They're beautiful, Amelia, just you wait!"

"But there are bangs!" she said, putting her hands over her ears. "Loud bangs! I don't like it!" It was a wail.

Caroline's heart sank. Poor Amelia was clearly not going to be persuaded. Large tears were glistening on her eyelids.

Caroline bent down and hugged her.

"It's all right, Amelia, everyone else can go, and you and I will stay here and look after Jasper. We'll lay the table so that when everyone comes back we can all eat the casserole I've made. How would that be?"

Amelia looked slightly mollified, and

went to find the puppy, who was sniffing around hopefully in the kitchen, drawn by the promising aroma of the casserole.

"It's not suppertime yet," Caroline heard the childish voice admonishing him. "Granny's already told you, you have to be patient and wait."

"Quite right," Caroline agreed. "When everyone else has gone, we can have some hot chocolate here, with marshmallows in. And we'll watch the fireworks through the window. Would you like that, Amelia?"

The little girl nodded, but her eyes were on her brothers, who were putting on wellies and coats and scarves, picking up torches and laughing happily as they searched for missing gloves.

"Are you sure you wouldn't like to come, sweetheart?" her father Dan asked, squatting down to her height. "We'll be lonely without you. Why don't you get your coat on? I'm sure Granny would like to come as well. And look…" he said, pulling a pair of bright pink earmuffs out of the glove drawer, "you could wear these, and then the bangs wouldn't be so loud."

He put them on himself, and Amelia
Continued overleaf

ILLUSTRATIONS: MANDY DIXON, ISTOCKPHOTO, REX/SHUTTERSTOCK

Continued from previous page

gave a weak smile but didn't giggle as she would normally have done.

"What do you think?" he asked.

But by way of an answer Amelia put her hands over her ears and ran straight out of the room.

"Sorry, Mum," Dan said. "Are you sure you don't mind staying with her? I could stay instead – I know how you love fireworks. You were always so excited about bonfire night when we were kids. It's a shame for you to miss them."

"We'll be fine," Caroline said, shaking her head. "There's no point in Amelia being frightened. I will have to take Jasper out in the garden – but briefly though, before the fireworks start. He's with

She was rewarded with the first proper smile of the evening. Children were easily pacified, she thought, smiling herself.

She was just adding the mini marshmallows to the two mugs when a loud bang heralded a rocket exploding.

"But the fireworks can't be starting yet," Caroline said frowning as she looked through the window. "That must be a different display. Or maybe someone nearby is having a firework party in their garden. Oh dear, Jasper, I'm afraid we'll have to go outside anyway. You can't wait until they're over."

The little dog had slunk into his basket, whimpering, and Amelia looked at him in alarm. Then she went over and put her arms round him.

The next bang and whoosh sent little Amelia scuttling out of the room

Amelia when it comes to loud noises…"

After yet more assurances that she and Amelia would be all right, and more frantic searching for a lost glove, Caroline finally saw the family off and went back into the kitchen where Amelia had returned to stroke Jasper.

"Is it time for hot chocolate yet?" Amelia asked at once.

"Well, I'm just going to take Jasper outside first."

"But that will take ages," Amelia said, her lip quivering again.

Caroline looked at the dog. "I dare say he can wait another few minutes," she said,then went to the fridge for some milk and set about heating it. "If we have a chocolate biscuit will you still be able to eat your supper?"

"It's OK, Jasper, they'll finish soon," she whispered, echoing what had been said to her so often. "You just have to be brave." She patted him, then nearly hit the ceiling as the next bang made her jump. "Oh no! I don't like this," she wailed, and Jasper began to howl in sympathy.

Caroline noticed that he was also fidgeting in an all too familiar way, and her heart sank.

"But he really needs to go outside, Amelia. He's only a puppy still, remember, and we don't want him to make a puddle in the kitchen, do we? Can you stay in here while I take him into the garden? Or maybe you could come out with us? That would make him happier."

Jasper whimpered pitifully, as though he understood every word.

The next bang and whoosh sent Amelia scuttling out of the room, but this time, rather than wailing she had her fingers in her ears and a look of grim determination on her face.

She returned a moment later, wearing the bright pink earmuffs her father had offered her earlier.

"Oh good, Amelia, you've put them on," Caroline said, smiling at her.

"What?" shouted Amelia. "I can't hear you!" and she suddenly laughed as the sky kaleidoscoped into colour once more. "Look, I found more in the drawer," she said excitedly. "They're for you, Jasper."

Unsurprisingly, Jasper was not keen on wearing earmuffs, especially when they kept falling down round his neck.

"But I'm wearing them, Jasper," Amelia wheedled. "They help, they really do. And the bangs are not as loud with them on… No," she said in a bossier, more grown-up voice, "You're not getting back in your basket. Come on, we've got to go outside. Granny says so."

She picked the puppy up as Caroline opened the back door.

They were not gone long. When the three of them came back into the kitchen even the puppy looked happier, particularly as Caroline declared it now was his suppertime.

"Do you want to feed him, Amelia?" she asked as she got out his food and refilled his water bowl.

Amelia, however, was glued to the window, watching the sky split into colour with each stream of rockets.

Caroline looked at her watch.

"You know, Amelia, the fireworks your mummy and daddy and the boys have gone to won't have started yet. If we put our coats on, we could still go and watch them. Jasper will be OK now that he's had his supper, and you'll be OK with your earmuffs on. Then you'll be able to see all the fireworks properly."

"And have more hot chocolate?"

"And have more hot chocolate," Caroline agreed, smiling.

How did you get her to come?" Dan asked later as Amelia sat on his shoulders, oohing and aahing with the rest of the crowd.

"A spot of bribery was involved," Caroline admitted, "But mostly it was down to Jasper. Having to comfort someone who's even more scared than you are does wonders for one's courage. At least, that's the way it was when *you* were frightened of the bangs at her age. You were absolutely terrified, remember? No, how could you? You were only four. And I really couldn't let you see how much I hated the bangs myself, could I?"

● ●

MY FAVOURITE

After reading it many years ago, I can never resist re-reading *The Chrysalids* by John Wyndham. I love disasters, and this story has such a human element. *Maggie Swinburne, Annual Editor.*

A Ripple
In Time

What if reality suddenly changed around you and everyone insisted you were mistaken?…

By Julia Douglas

J o knew nothing of quantum physics. She didn't really care what the scientists at STERN were doing with their Sub-atomic Particle Collider in the miles and miles of tunnels, deep beneath Geneva.

"The fools will make a black hole and destroy the world!" Pierre's eyes twinkled with amusement as he showed her his newspaper.

Jo laughed at his nonsense as she carried their plates to the kitchen.

In the doorway, she stopped dead. A strange man was standing at the counter, making coffee.

"Who are you?" she demanded.

He gave her a quizzical smile, steaming kettle poised above the jug.

"Why – who did you think I was?" he asked, mildly.

Something about his relaxed smile and ironically raised eyebrow transfixed her. His features and stance tugged at something deep in her memory. Her eyes flicked over the lines around his friendly hazel eyes and his slightly receding, greying hair, cut short and neat.

Jo gripped the used dinner plates she was carrying and shouted over her shoulder. "Pierre, come here!"

There was no answer. The man in the kitchen put down the kettle.

"Jo," he said, "are you OK?"

The plates crashed to the floor and smashed, as she backed away from him.

"Get away from me!"

Jo ran into the dining room.

"Pierre, where are you?" She searched the room frantically, and ran into the hall.

"Pierre!" she yelled, desperately.

"Who are you talking to?" The man from the kitchen now looked frightened and confused.

Jo backed against the banisters of the stairs, trapped. "Where's my husband?"

"*I'm* your husband!" The stranger gripped her arms. "Look at me, Jo! It's me – Jack!"

Shaking, Jo stared at the so-familiar eyes in a face that had aged thirty years.

"But you're… you're *dead!*"

She fainted into his arms.

A streak of lightning ripped through the city sky, and the rain came down in sheets. Drivers turned on their headlights as rain bounced off their cars. Pedestrians held newspapers over their heads, fumbled with umbrellas or ran for cover as the deluge fell upon them.

Elise stumbled disorientated into a **Continued overleaf**

Continued from previous page

doorway, the total soaking making every nerve in her body zing like an electric shock. Her head felt as if it was trapped in a vice. It was worse than the worst hangover she'd ever had – and in her student days, she'd had a few.

Her stomach was churning. But as her breathing and heartbeat receded from heart attack levels, she could have danced with joy.

It had worked! She was alive! She was…

Elise didn't know where she was, but she certainly wasn't at STERN.

Instinctively she checked the devices on her wrists and ankles; the control unit on her belt that would take her back – she hoped.

But where was she?

Gathering her wits, Elise looked out at the traffic. The cars were big and American. There were yellow cabs among them. It looked like New York. But when?

Across the street, she saw a newsstand.

Impulsively, she ran into the rain. Still disorientated, she didn't see the car skidding towards her until it was too late.

Jo was supposed to be lying down, but how was she supposed to relax?

She sat up in the darkened bedroom and clicked on the bedside light.

With trembling fingers, she once again picked up the framed picture from the bedside table and stared with red-raw eyes at the smiling family group.

The blonde woman was herself, in her thirties. The man was a younger version of the man she'd just met in her kitchen. He looked more like the Jack she knew – the young fiancé who'd been so cruelly taken from her.

Who were the children? A boy and girl that looked a bit like her and a bit like Jack. How could she have forgotten the faces of her own children?

No – that was wrong. She couldn't let herself start believing that.

Heart pounding, Jo put the frame face down, not wanting to look at it.

She and Pierre didn't have children. That was the second great tragedy of her life, after losing Jack.

Yet Pierre, her hearty Frenchman, understood what it meant to her. He'd been there for her through the unsuccessful rounds of IVF. She'd clung to him like a rock and it had brought them even closer.

She pictured Pierre's lovely, kind face, smiling at her across the dinner table, just moments before she carried the plates into the kitchen and everything changed.

Downstairs, she heard the front door open, and hushed voices.

"Thanks so much for coming over. It's probably nothing, but after what happened thirty years ago…"

Footsteps came up the stairs and the man who called himself Jack, and who looked strangely like Jack might have done if he'd lived another thirty years, came into the bedroom. He was followed by a blessedly familiar face.

"Oh, Tom – I'm so glad you're here!" Jo almost threw herself into his arms. "Pierre has disappeared! I don't know what's happening!"

NYC♥

"Pierre?" Her old friend exchanged a puzzled look with Jack.

"My husband!" Jo almost screamed. "Your best friend!"

Tom gently shook his head.

"Jack's your husband, Jo. I should know. I was his best man, remember? I don't know anyone called Pierre."

Jo stared in horror from Tom to Jack

"Am I going mad, Tom?"

"No," the family friend reassured her. "It's just like that time after the plane crash when you were sure that Jack was dead and couldn't adjust to him coming back. Do you remember that little breakdown you had?"

"You refused to believe I was me." Jack laughed nervously. "You were

"I've found her!" Tyler burst in. "She's become a conspiracy theory!"

and back again. In spite of herself, she knew there was something intrinsically Jack-like about the grey-haired newcomer. She was trying to fight the long-buried feelings he stirred in her.

"But Jack's dead!" she insisted. "I remember the plane crash, the funeral…"

Tom nodded sympathetically.

"You remember the plane crash, but Jack wasn't on the plane… do you remember that now?"

"I missed the flight," Jack reminded her, softly. "I was snarled up in traffic. Some sort of accident. I was stuck there for hours – thankfully."

"You thought he was dead," said Tom. "For a day there, we all did. But he came home, Jo. Look at him – he's right here."

Jo pressed her fingers to her temples.

"I remember the funeral. You were there, Tom! You were there when I married Pierre! I have the photographs!"

Of course, she didn't. Jo stared, bereft, at the photo albums she'd thrown on the carpet earlier. There wasn't a single snap of Pierre – just a full colour record of a life with Jack and their children, of which she didn't remember a moment.

convinced that I was an impostor…"

"You were fine after a few weeks," Tom cut in quickly. "I'm sure it's just a little relapse of that."

I've found her!" Tyler burst into the boardroom. The top brass were in fierce debate but no one resented the interruption – things were way too serious for that.

"She's become a conspiracy theory!" Tyler's face was contorted with anguish as he ran up to the chairman and thrust a computer tablet in front of him.

He started a YouTube video and a Californian teenager with geeky glasses began to speak.

"Yo, truth seekers, this week we ask: did a time traveller die in New York in 1987?"

The chairman took a sharp breath as an old newspaper clipping flashed onto the screen. The grainy black and white picture was a mortuary photo of a young woman, beautiful even in death.

"Elise," Tyler breathed.

"The woman who was killed in a traffic **Continued overleaf** accident has never been identified," the YouTuber continued. "But a retired paramedic who attended the scene insists that she was wearing some kind of technology he'd never seen before and – get this, guys – carrying Swiss coins dated 2017. The authorities, of course, deny all of this…"

Tyler stopped the video. "We've got to go back and get her. Stop this happening."

"It's too dangerous," the vice-chairman broke in. "We could change history."

"It's already changed." Tyler glared at him. "Look at your coffee cup."

The whole board gazed at the white paper cup with its distinctive green logo.

"Tell me. When was it ever called

"As you are aware, it will take a month for the Collider to generate enough energy for another leap."

A re you feeling better now, Mum?" "Yes, Charlotte – honestly, please don't worry about me."

"I wish I could come home and be with you awhile."

"No, it's OK, Charlotte. Your job's important. I'm… very proud of you."

Jo ended the transatlantic call and took a deep breath. She stroked the phone's screen with a trembling thumb and brought up a photo of the daughter she'd never met; never even knew she had.

How is it possible? she wondered, for the millionth time. Yet she'd seen the

"Thanks for being patient with me. I still love you. I never stopped loving you"

Star Cups?" Tyler demanded.

"Ripples in time," mused Hogan, the chief scientist. "One road accident causes someone to miss a meeting, so a coffee chain gets a different name. How many other small changes ripple outwards?"

"It's not just small changes," the chairman snapped. "America has a different president."

"Perhaps we should just leave things as they are?" the vice-chairman ventured.

"People will notice!" said the chairman.

"Send me back to save her," Tyler pleaded. "Let me put things back the way they were."

He picked up the tablet and stared at the frozen image of Elise's dead face. "She's my fiancée!" he said dully.

The chairman nodded, tight-lipped.

photographs. Herself and her children as they grew up. Birthdays, holidays, graduation days – every milestone. How could she have forgotten it all?

Jo felt instinctively that Charlotte was her daughter. She could see so much of herself in the girl's face – and so much of Jack, too.

And Jack was Jack. He'd aged, as she had, but he was unmistakably the same sweet guy she was certain she'd lost in a plane crash thirty years ago.

Letting the phone rest in her lap, Jo turned to him, where he sat beside her on the sunny park bench.

"How are you feeling?" he enquired.

"I'm fine." Jo sighed.

For what was the alternative, except to commit herself to a lunatic asylum by

insisting the whole world had changed overnight?

Jack and Tom said she'd been briefly under psychiatric care thirty years ago after the double trauma of believing Jack was dead, then learning he was alive.

She didn't remember it, but perhaps she did have a history of mental illness and this was a relapse.

Jack had certainly thought she was nuts when she told him where she worked. Somehow he'd convinced her not to go to the office and make a fool of herself. So she'd Googled the managing director of the bank – and, to her horror, it wasn't her. How could it have been, when she'd apparently spent her life devoted to family, not work?

They all thought she'd lost her memory. But Jo knew it wasn't simple amnesia, because she had thirty years of completely different memories. Her first sight of Pierre, their courtship and marriage, their love and laughter.

She could see it all as clear as day. She missed her Frenchman with all her soul. How could she have conjured up such vivid experiences in her imagination?

Jo was certain her memory was true and everything else had changed, because every day her eye was snagged by a reminder of how the world had altered.

Clinton was the American president, and everyone laughed when Jo swore that Trump won the election. Just as they smiled indulgently when she told them the coffee chain was supposed to be called Starbucks.

Just last night, she'd re-watched a favourite film with Jack, and found that one of the actors was different.

It was as if she was in another world. But with no way out, what could she do but accept her situation?

Jo had been wary of Jack for the past month, slowly getting to know him again.

But now, in the sunny park, where everything except her seemed so normal, she took his hand.

"Thanks for being patient with me," she told him. "I still love you. I never stopped loving you."

He leaned in to kiss her – then someone caught her eye.

"Pierre!" Jo leapt up and ran across the grass. "Pierre! Where have you been?"

Pierre turned with a smile. But it was just the ready smile he'd have for anyone who called his name. As Jo neared, she realised he was with a wife and children she'd never seen before.

"I'm sorry, madame," the Frenchman said. "Do I know you?"

Continued overleaf

A crack of lightning ripped through the black cloud over the city. Elise ran from the doorway into the torrential rain.

"Elise!"

A hand caught her arm just as she was about to step off the kerb. She spun around into a man's embrace as a car shot past and sprayed them with water.

"Tyler! What are you doing here?"

"Taking you home."

Tyler pressed the buttons on her control device and his, and the entwined couple dissolved into the rain.

A moment later, a cab went by with Jack in the back. He was glad the traffic was light. He'd have no trouble catching his plane.

H ey Jo, come and look at this!" Pierre pulled his laptop around on the table so his wife could see. "I bet those fools at STERN are behind it!"

Jo chuckled indulgently as she crossed the room. Happy to be back with him, she put her arms around his shoulders and rubbed the side of her face against his as she looked at the screen.

"Yo, truth seekers," a Californian teenager with geeky glasses was saying. "This week we ask: did we spend a month living in an alternative universe?

"Crazy though it sounds, we've been getting reports of some very weird happenings. Get this, guys: some folks swear we even had a different president…"

"Do you believe in that?" Jo asked, softly. "Alternative universes?"

She hadn't told Pierre anything about the month she'd spent in what she was trying to convince herself had been a dream. It had been bad enough feeling that she was nuts in that world, without having people think she was nuts in this one as well.

"Alternative universes, time travel…" Pierre chuckled. "Who knows what those quantum fools at STERN might be tampering with!"

Jo turned his chin towards her and kissed him, long and gratefully.

In the twenty years they'd been together, their love had grown into something she would never swap.

It wasn't the life she'd thought she'd have, but it was the life she'd lived, and she was proud of what she'd made of it.

Yet it was true what she'd told Jack, too. She'd never stopped loving him, and never would.

Many a night in the small hours, she'd lain awake and wondered what their life together would have been like if he had lived. She'd wondered, too, how it would have felt to have children, and to watch them grow up and have successful lives.

She felt lighter knowing that on some other plane, another version of her had shared that life with Jack… and maybe still was.

• •

MY FAVOURITE…

My favourite guilty pleasure is watching conspiracy theory videos on YouTube. There's one called *The Mandela Effect* that claims time-travellers have changed history from the way we remember it…

Brain BOOSTERS SOLUTIONS

CODEWORD FROM PAGE 27

PHRASE: MELANIE GRIFFITH AND DON JOHNSON

KRISS KROSS FROM PAGE 35

R	A	D	D	L	E	D		K	E	R	B
A		U		I				I		E	
G	A	S	S	Y		V		T	I	D	Y
B		T		E	M	I	G	R	E		O
A		P		A		S					U
G	O	A	T	S	K	I	N		T	U	B	A

(Kriss Kross grid)

R	A	D	D	L	E	D			K	E	R	B
A		U		I					I		E	
G	A	S	S	Y		V			T	I	D	Y
B		T		E	M	I	G	R	E		O	
A		P		A		S					U	
G	O	A	T	S	K	I	N		T	U	B	A
		N		T		O		S			L	
	G				N	A	T	I	V	E		
	R		D			A		O				
F	O	R	L	O	R	N		T	A	U	T	
	V		U		A		U		C			
	E		S	T	R	E	T	C	H	Y		
S	L	A	K	E		K		E				

MISSING LINK FROM PAGE 45

ACROSS: 2 Cabin 7 Full 8 Trap 9 Arc 10 Person 11 Looked 13 Blade 14 Answer 15 Far 16 Treble 18 Emery 21 Socket 23 Return 25 Ham 26 Vein 27 Easy 28 Rider
DOWN: 1 Cube 2 Closed 3 Brand 4 Nuclear 5 Stools 6 Hare 12 Dirty 13 Bites 15 Feather 17 Baking 19 Mother 20 Armed 22 Oven 24 Rise
SHADED WORD: CANDID

MISSING LINK FROM PAGE 57

ACROSS: 1 Town 3 Primary 9 Kitchen 10 Stall 11 Roman 13 Swing 14 Kind 16 Extra 18 Bags 19 Pedal 21 Syrup 23 Lease 24 Treated 25 Density 26 Eyed
DOWN: 1 Takers 2 Watering 4 Ran 5 Mason 6 Real 7 Charge 8 Flood 12 Motor 15 Industry 17 Apples 18 Bully 20 Landed 21 Sheds 22 Date 24 Tit
SHADED WORD: TICKLE

SUDOKU 1 FROM PAGE 101

3	1	6	2	9	7	4	8	5
9	5	7	4	8	1	6	3	2
8	2	4	5	3	6	7	1	9
1	3	2	6	4	5	8	9	7
5	6	9	7	2	8	3	4	1
4	7	8	9	1	3	2	5	6
7	9	1	3	6	4	5	2	8
6	8	3	1	5	2	9	7	4
2	4	5	8	7	9	1	6	3

SUDOKU 2 FROM PAGE 101

9	5	2	7	6	1	8	4	3
1	4	6	3	8	5	2	9	7
8	7	3	2	9	4	5	6	1
6	2	4	1	3	9	7	8	5
5	8	9	4	2	7	3	1	6
3	1	7	8	5	6	4	2	9
4	6	5	9	7	8	1	3	2
2	9	8	5	1	3	6	7	4
7	3	1	6	4	2	9	5	8

WORD WHEEL FROM PAGE 101 The nine-letter word is SWEETCORN

Follow My Lead

Ulterior motives or not, it seems Louisa's neighbour's plan for a dog obedience class is a good one...

By Lisa Allen

I t's a bright summer's day and the sun's rays are already tickling the flowers and foliage gently awake.

Louisa brushes her hand over the petals and takes a deep breath, filling her senses with the relaxing scent of French roses, jasmine and lavender. *Today's going to be a good day,* she tells herself.

A bee darts through the air, skittering between flowers, drawn to the rich pickings of nectar they offer. Rufus, Louisa's eight-year-old cocker spaniel, spots it, bounding across the garden playfully, almost knocking her over.

"Rufus! We don't have time for games. Our first class will be arriving soon."

Rufus gives his owner a nonchalant look with his big brown eyes then wags his tail. Louisa can't help laughing.

She hadn't been entirely convinced that offering a dog training class, at her house, was a good idea. But her retired neighbour, Janet, talked her into it.

Too late to change my mind now, she thinks resignedly, watching Rufus dig a hole next to her roses.

"Rufus! Stop it." He looks up sulkily then skulks away. Louisa rolls her eyes. "I hope you're not going to show me up today, in front of everyone."

Rufus ignores her.

Louisa follows him back to the patio. Her eyes flick across a list of names Janet has provided. There will be eight people and their dogs.

Bubbles of nerves spin in her tummy. She looks to Rufus, but he's now soaking

up the sunshine, oblivious.

Moving to the village had felt strange at first. She missed her parents and her old friends. But it felt good to have a fresh start after getting divorced. Her neighbour, Janet, had been wonderful, helping them settle in.

"It was a wrench leaving everything behind. Mum is constantly worrying about me," Louisa confided to Janet one afternoon over tea. "But I know I made the right decision. It just takes time to adjust, doesn't it?"

"Of course it does, love," Janet agreed, patting her arm. "Life will fall into place, you mark my words."

Janet looked down at Rufus, who was concentrating hard on the last piece of biscuit in her hand.

"And you're a lovely dog – so well behaved," observed Janet adoringly, offering the biscuit to Rufus. He gingerly accepted the treat and gave a triumphant sideways glance at Louisa.

She arched her eyebrow in retort.

"You clearly haven't seen the mound of primroses he dug up last week."

They laughed.

Louisa rubbed Rufus' ears affectionately. "He is a good boy most of the time, aren't you? He should be anyway, seeing as I used to be a dog trainer," Louisa admitted, laughing as she ruffled his fur affectionately.

Janet's eyes lit up.

"Really? Well now that is interesting."

"Is it?"

"Oh yes. We're in need of a dog trainer round here. I know that for a fact, because my son is the local vet," Janet announced proudly. "In fact, you could run a class here."

They gazed at the beautifully manicured lawn and colourful flowers in Louisa's new garden. She'd had a lot of time on her hands lately. With savings in the bank, she hadn't been in any hurry to get a new job.

"Here?" Louisa repeated, unsure.

"It would be perfect," said Janet, with a flourish of her hand. "I can help with refreshments. We'll just invite some people from the village – you'll meet some new people," she paused, considering, "and maybe get a little business going? Win-win, dearie."

Win-win? Louisa's heart sank. She hadn't bargained on this. What if she made a fool of herself?

She glanced down at Rufus. He fixed her with a gaze, doe-eyed. It was as if he was reading her mind, willing her to give it a go.

She shrugged. "Oh, what the heck, let's go for it."

"Fabulous!" Janet clapped her hands.

Continued overleaf

Continued from previous page

And now dog training day has arrived. *At least it's sunny*, thinks Louisa nervously, while Janet busies herself lining up glasses of squash on the patio table, like soldiers in a row.

"Knock, knock." A shrill voice echoes around the garden. A rotund woman with curly hair bustles through the side gate, followed by a short-haired Dachshund.

"Welcome," says Louisa, waving them over. She pauses, scanning her list. "Is it Lorna? And this must be Dudley." She smiles warmly.

"Yes, that's right. But I'll say now, I don't hold out much hope for this training class, mind," she replies briskly. She looks down at Dudley dubiously. "There's a saying; you can't teach an old dog new tricks."

Dudley frowns from underneath his wispy eyebrows.

"Oh, I don't know," Louisa replies cheerily. "Dudley looks like he could learn some new tricks, hey, buddy?"

"I was talking about me, luvvie," laughs Lorna, bustling past to see Janet. Dudley shuffles along behind her, begrudgingly.

Louisa gulps. She hopes the next few people will be a bit more positive, otherwise this has the potential to be a complete disaster.

To her relief, a very jolly man called Frank and his schnauzer, Gordon, are next to trundle through the gate. Followed by Denise and her Yorkshire terrier, Petal, then Yvette and her Westie, Wilbert.

"Been really looking forward to this," exclaims Frank.

"Oh yes, Wilbert too. He's very intelligent, you know. I'm sure he will pick things up very quickly."

"Petal and I can never turn down the offer of free biscuits!"

Louisa relaxes, pleased that her new arrivals seemed to be cheery and hopefully not too demanding.

They are shortly followed by three more locals and their dogs from the village, who make a beeline for the refreshments table.

I'll give them all ten minutes to chat, Louisa decides. *Hopefully that will ease them into the training class*. She glances at Janet who is in her element as hostess.

"Hi. Louisa?" A voice from behind makes her jump.

Distractedly, Louisa turns round, dropping her list of attendee names on the grass. Rufus, not one to miss an opportunity for mischief, pounces on it with his muddy paws, and rips it to shreds in front of them.

"Rufus, no!" Louisa looks at him with dismay as he wags his tail naughtily, and runs off with half the list.

"You must be the dog trainer," says the man, with a wry smile.

Her cheeks redden, blinking at him through the glare of the sun. He is disarmingly attractive and suddenly she is at a loss of what to say.

"Oh. Um, yes. I am."

"I'm Harry." He dazzles her with a smile.

Is it the heat from the sun, or is she having some kind of hot flush?

She notices a black Labrador standing at his side patiently. Following her line of gaze Harry elaborates, "Oh yes, and this here is Wolf."

"Hi, Wolf," she says softly, bending

down to give him a pat. "He doesn't look as if he needs much training," she comments, noticing his calm manner and intelligent eyes. She glances up at Harry.

He grins. "Well, he could do with some pointers on food etiquette. Has a bit of a habit of stealing it. Specifically my lunch. He wolfs it down. Hence the name, Wolf."

They laugh.

Louisa instantly warms to Harry. He is clearly good-looking, with short wavy black hair, and dark eyes that crinkle when he laughs. But more than that, she feels very relaxed in his presence. As if she can be herself.

"Well, I'll see what I can do. But I can't

says. "OK, everyone. Gather round." Louisa waves over her guests and they form a little group.

"Dudley only works for cheese," announces Lorna from the back, taking a gulp of squash. There are a few murmurs of laughter.

"Well, luckily I have a mixture of dog treats, including some cheese cubes. Now, I've set up a short course along here," she gestures to the line of orange cones on the lawn. "And what I'm going to ask you to do is walk your dog, keeping them at your side, in and out of these cones. This is a good warm-up exercise to get them in training mode.

"He could do with some pointers on food etiquette. He keeps stealing my lunch"

promise anything. Labs can be incurable scroungers." She stands up, meeting his eyes. He smiles.

"OK, well, I'm expecting results. Mum said you were the best." He nods in the direction of Janet, who waves at them from amongst the other guests.

"Oh, you're Janet's son? The vet?" She is surprised. Janet hasn't mentioned he was one of the guests.

He puts his hand over his face briefly, embarrassed. "I should have my name changed by deed poll to 'My Son The Vet'." He shakes his head. "Mum is what you could call an overly proud parent."

Louisa giggles. She appreciates it when a man can be self-deprecating. It shows a humorous side. Something her ex-husband could certainly have done with, she reflects.

"Well we'd better get started," she

You can use treats if you need to."

They all line up, ready.

"Right," says Louisa, clipping Rufus' lead onto his collar. "Rufus and I will demonstrate first. Just follow my lead."

An hour later, an exhausted Louisa is slumped in one of the garden chairs.

"That was great." Harry hands her a drink. "You have a great rapport with people. And the dogs, too."

Louisa blushes. "Thanks."

Harry pulls up a chair next to her, as Janet beckons the others over to the patio for sandwiches.

"You know, we could really do with someone like you up at the vet's practice." He leans forward, smiling. Louisa's heart does a little somersault.

"Would you think about running a few **Continued overleaf**

classes for us? See if there is much uptake? I'm sure there would be."

She raises her eyebrows in disbelief.

"Really? I mean, I would love to. But would there be much interest?"

"Definitely." He looks at her intently. "Actually, I have to confess something."

"Oh?" Louisa looks at him quizzically.

"If you hadn't already guessed, Mum sort of orchestrated this little event. So that we could meet."

Louisa's heart sinks rapidly. She knew it was all turning out to be too good to be true. Attractive, funny men seemingly interested in her don't just appear. She suddenly feels more than a little foolish.

"But I'm really glad she did," Harry adds hurriedly, noticing her expression.

"You are?" she whispered.

"I am. Mum can be really meddlesome sometimes, but she means well. And on this occasion she was right."

"Right about what?"

He takes her hand in his and squeezes it gently.

"You, Louisa, are absolutely perfect."

She thinks her heart might just melt with happiness.

"You're not so bad yourself," she grins, disengaging her hand shyly.

"So maybe we could go for dinner sometime? Talk about the new dog training classes?" He gives a hopeful look.

"I'd like that very much, actually," she replies, smiling.

Janet suddenly appears with a plate of sandwiches. "And how are things going over here?" Her eyes glint mischievously.

They look at each other and laugh.

"What?" demands Janet, pretending to look affronted.

Suddenly, Rufus starts barking out on the patio, alerting Louisa to the fact that her mobile phone is ringing.

"Excuse me a sec, I'd probably better answer that."

Harry nods. She grins to herself, listening to Janet's voice complaining about Wolf stealing a sandwich, as she hurries over to answer the phone.

"Hi, Mum."

"Hello, Louisa love. I just thought I would see how you're doing? I worry about you all on your own in a strange place, with just that dopey dog for company."

Louisa smiles. Rufus has everyone wrapped round his little paw – including her mother, come to that.

"I told you, Mum, we're absolutely fine. Actually we're holding a little gathering today – just a few people from the village," she says, looking round at the garden full of happy faces, and dogs running around. "It's been really nice."

"That's good. But you still need to get out and meet people, and find a job. Jobs and relationships don't just turn up on your doorstep, Louisa."

Louisa glances across at Harry. He smiles broadly at her, raising his glass.

"Oh, I don't know…" Louisa grins. "Sometimes they do."

MY FAVOURITE…

My current favourite book is *The Help* by Kathryn Stockett. Strong, warm women learning to trust each other and achieve something amazing.
Sarah Proctor, sub-editor

FANCY THAT!

Fascinating Facts **In The Air!**

✦ Plane toilet doors don't actually lock, as crew need to be able to access them from outside in emergencies!

✦ The oxygen mask that drops down in emergencies contains 15-20 minutes of oxygen – the time it takes an aircraft to descend to an altitude of 10,000 feet with breathable air.

✦ **Amelia Mary Earhart was the first woman to fly solo across the Atlantic Ocean in 1928.**

The world's oldest airline is Dutch carrier KLM, established in 1919

✦ The chances of being killed in a plane crash are only 1 in 4.7 million – less than being killed by an asteroid impact!

✦ **Sally Ride was the first American woman to fly into space on board space shuttle Challenger.**

✦ In 1987 American Airlines, keen to reduce costs, saved $40,000 by simply removing one olive from each salad served in first class. Food for thought!

✦ Due to supersonic heating at Mach 2 speed, Concorde's airframe stretched by 6-10 inches on every flight!

✦ **Only 5% of the world's population has ever been on an aeroplane.**

✦ Sheila Scott, born in Worcestershire in 1922, broke more than 100 aviation records between 1965 and 1972, from flying solo over the north Pole to flying solo around the world.

✦ **At any one time there are 3 million people on planes in the air. They may share that space with bumblebees, which have been spotted at 18,000 feet high!**

Snow Angel

After meeting gorgeous Florin at a fancy dress party,
Nikki was astonished to find out his real profession…

By Tess Niland Kimber

THE new year was only a week old but already proving fab, Nikki thought, checking her phone for another text from Florin. She wasn't disappointed.

Coffee? Or is that too boring to suggest?

Coffee would be great! she'd pinged back – leaving her reply for a whole three minutes so she didn't look too keen.

The problem was, she was keen – *very* keen. They'd met on a riverboat on New Year's Eve. How romantic was that!

She'd been invited to the party by a friend of a friend.

"Go on, Nikki. Food's always fabulous. Jenna and Greg really know how to party," her friend Mimi offered. "Cheryl and I are going. You'll love it. Besides, you're not doing anything else, are you?"

"No," she'd shrugged.

Since her last boyfriend, she'd given up dating. It was OK; she liked her own company and her job as a statistician kept her busy. She didn't need a boyfriend, she'd thought throughout the past year, but over Christmas and New Year she'd began to feel a Plus One might be handy.

Being alone, she'd turned down several festive invitations, but when Mimi and her partner Cheryl invited her to Jenna and Greg's New Year party, she was seriously tempted.

Jenna worked with Mimi at the hospital. Nikki had met her a few times but couldn't claim to know her, and had never met Greg, her investment banker husband. But Mimi insisted; with nothing planned, New Year curled up in front of the telly would be too depressing.

The party was to be held on Jenna and Greg's riverboat, sailing down the River Arun, seeing in the New Year under a canopy of fireworks. It sounded amazing. But Nikki almost backed out when she heard those two words guaranteed to strike fear into her heart – Fancy Dress.

"But it's easy!" Mimi had assured her. "It's occupational. Go as a plumber, doctor, even a checkout girl."

It hadn't been easy for Nikki. She'd struggled to come up with an outfit that wasn't frumpy or tarty. But then, sudden inspiration had struck – she could go as an air hostess!

Boarding Married Bliss – Jenna and Greg's riverboat – Nikki felt a million dollars in her red jacket and skirt combo with pillbox hat. The boat was so glamorous. A wide deck curved around the glass interior. In the lounge, delicate canapés filled silver platters and waiters dressed in tails wandered through the crowd offering flutes of champagne and orange juice.

But as she searched for her friends, her

phone buzzed. It was Mimi.

Sorry to let you down, Nik. Cheryl's got the lurgy. Happy New Year!

Oh no! Now she'd be alone. She only knew Jenna, who made a convincing waitress, but from her body language it seemed she wasn't currently enjoying "Married Bliss" with Greg, who was dressed as a policeman.

Nikki sighed. Just as she planned to make her excuses and leave, someone bumped into her, spilling her champagne.

"Oh, I'm so sorry! Will you let me get you another drink?"

The man was tall with wavy blond hair, sea-green eyes and dressed as a vicar.

She was about to refuse, but then thought – *why not?* It was New Year's Eve and although it wasn't how she would have chosen it, she'd broken the ice and spoken to someone. One more drink, before she left, wouldn't hurt.

The man brought her a fresh glass of champagne and some canapés on a plate.

"I thought I'd take a chance to grab some food," he explained.

Nikki smiled, thanking him.

"Parties aren't my thing normally," he confessed, "but Greg made me come along tonight… and I'm very glad I did."

She smiled. It was the first time a "vicar" had chatted her up.

Finding a vacant sofa, they sat down and Florin introduced himself.

The dance floor was packed.

"Do you like dancing?" he asked.

"Only when I've had a few of these." She laughed, waving her glass. "Not that I'm a big drinker – I just mean that I have two left feet. How about you?"

"Only dad dancing – although I'm not a father. Sorry, I'm out of practice. I love talking – I'm just not good at this sort of talking."

Nikki smiled. There was something

Continued overleaf

Continued from previous page

attractive about Florin. He was a breath of fresh air – a man who admitted his flaws instead of playing Mr Cool.

"Well, forget that sort of talking – just talk." She smiled. "Where are you from?"

"Parish of St Joseph's."

She giggled. He was good at this fancy dress game; he'd even taken on the personality of a vicar.

"Me, too. I'm Elmside."

"Lovely part of town… So you're an air hostess?"

"I wish – no, I'm a statistician."

"OK, that sounds… interesting."

everyone!" shouted Greg and Jenna, who'd thankfully made up.

On the deck, Nikki watched the fireworks light up the inky sky.

"Happy 2018, Nikki," Florin said, gently brushing her lips with his own.

New Year's Eve was the most spellbinding night Nikki could remember. At the end of the evening, they exchanged mobile numbers and she'd been delighted to wake to a text from him.

Thank you for a super evening. Best I've had in ages.

That day texts flurried between them.

It was so romantic sailing down the river, dancing, eating, drinking and talking

"It is. I collect data and work out the likelihood of risk. I love it."

He smiled. "That's great – we should all do what we enjoy."

"And you?"

The music stopped but before Florin could answer, Greg announced over the microphone, "We're casting off. Soon it'll be the New Year countdown and we'll watch fireworks further down river."

"Wow! This is fantastic." Nikki beamed in delight, looking for Jenna and hoping her row with Greg wasn't serious.

"Isn't it?" Florin said, holding her gaze for a moment longer than necessary. Her spine tingled. She hadn't felt like this for years.

Her plan to go home forgotten, the evening passed in a blur. It was so romantic sailing down the river, dancing, eating delicious food and talking to Florin.

"Three, two, one. Happy New Year,

Over the next week they'd got to know each other more. It felt like an old-fashioned courtship conducted through modern technology.

Now Nikki was thrilled Florin had invited her for coffee, but she didn't know what to wear. Jeans and jumper would work but as he'd liked her red air hostess outfit, she decided to wear her red winter coat and boots. She'd take her red umbrella, too, as the sky was brooding – full of possible snow. The weather forecasters had threatened it for days but other than some heavy frosts, not a flake had fallen.

Where shall we meet? Nikki texted just before she set off.

Do you know St Joseph's Church by Orchard Road? There's a great café near there, he replied.

So she set off for the church, thinking it was a handy landmark.

It was very cold. By the time she reached Bolland Square, the first flakes started to fall. Should she text Florin and go home? But checking her phone, she didn't have a signal. She'd better carry on. He might think she'd stood him up on their first proper date.

The beautiful gothic church was silhouetted against the falling snow which swirled around her like white feathers. Shivering, she waited on the church path. *Hurry up, Florin*, she thought. It was cold and dark. Just about to turn and walk home, she heard a voice.

"Nikki!"

It was Florin, dressed in a black padded jacket.

"You must be freezing. Come on."

Wrapping his arm around her shoulders, he ducked under the shelter of her red umbrella. Instantly, she felt warmer, held against him.

She imagined he was heading to George Street where there were numerous cafés, but he surprised her, leading her towards the church.

"I wanted to take you to Drury's. They do a mean cappuccino but as it's snowing, we'd better stay here. It's warm and the coffee's good even if I say so myself."

Too cold to argue, Nikki followed him down a stone passageway to a door which opened into a modern lounge with plump sofas, a roaring log burner and large flat screen TV.

"Coffee? Tea? Hot chocolate? I think I've marshmallows somewhere."

"Here? Don't they mind?"

"Why should they?" Florin said, unzipping his jacket and revealing his dog collar.

"But you…? You really are a vicar?"

He smiled. "Yes. Does it bother you?"

"Yes, I mean no, of course not," Nikki floundered and was thankful when he disappeared to make their drinks.

While he was away her mind went into overdrive. A vicar! She'd been sharing some seriously flirty texts with the local clergyman!

She flushed as red as her coat. She wasn't religious and couldn't remember the last time she'd been to church, but she liked Florin. Really liked him. Although they'd only just met, she was now worried how they could possibly make a relationship work when there was such a fundamental difference between them?

Florin returned, carrying a tray with mugs of hot chocolate and a plate of scrummy-looking flapjacks.

"Wow! Just what we need."

Putting the tray on the coffee table, he sprawled onto the sofa opposite. She couldn't help thinking how incredibly good-looking he was. More like a famous actor than a vicar. But she felt uneasy and he picked up the vibe.

"It bothers you, doesn't it, Nikki? Me being a vicar."

"It's a shock. I thought you were in fancy dress. I didn't realise you'd come straight from work." She sipped her hot chocolate nervously. "I'll go soon. The snow might lie."

"I understand," he said, looking utterly miserable.

When she'd finished her hot chocolate,

Continued overleaf

she broke off a corner of flapjack.

"Delicious!" she exclaimed, suprised.

"Another of my many talents – well, my only one, actually."

She laughed. He was so easy to talk to. No doubt he made a great vicar. But as a boyfriend? She didn't know…

Her mug empty, she stood to leave.

"I'll slip on my wellies and walk you home. I'll find you a pair, too." He looked at her high heeled boots, great for shopping but not for hiking through snow.

"Thanks, but I don't want to put you out."

"It's no problem. And if you borrow the boots you'll have to come back to return them." He gave her a cheeky grin before disappearing. Returning a few minutes later, he handed over some green wellies.

"They're probably too big so I brought you a couple of pairs of my football socks as well," he explained.

She laughed. "They are a bit big – but better than my high heels."

He was so lovely. *If only…* she thought, confused.

Opening the outer door, she was shocked by the depth of the snow.

"Are you quite sure you want to walk me home in this?"

"Of course," he insisted.

They set off, Florin carrying her boots in a bag. *My snow angel,* she thought. He linked arms with her and she instantly felt that tingle. He must have felt it too for he looked down at her and smiled.

As they walked, they talked.

"So you're into football?"

"Yes, I love it. Can't play in the Sunday league, of course, but most Saturdays I'm at Kipling Park, trying to score a hat-trick."

"Hmmm. I really can't imagine a vicar playing football."

"I'm a man, too, you know… Come and watch me when you're free."

She smiled. "I'd like that."

A man, too. The phrase hummed in her head as they trudged through the snow, their arms threaded. No matter what he did for a living, what his beliefs were, he was a man. A man she'd love to see again.

It took them an hour to reach her flat.

"Come in for coffee. You must be freezing," she said.

"OK." He smiled. "Have you got any flapjacks?"

"Sorry. Only leftover Christmas cake."

"I think I'll pass. There's a few things I could tackle my boss about. Along with world poverty and child cruelty, dried-up turkey and Christmas cake are on the list."

She laughed, showing him into the tiny lounge.

"This is nice." He smiled. "Very rustic."

"Thank you," she said, seeing the room through his eyes. Sandwiched between two squashy cream sofas with coloured cushions was a log burner. Her brother had laid a real oak floor and in front of the fire was a sheepskin rug. On the low coffee table was her only concession to the festive season – a miniature Christmas tree beautifully decorated with crystal baubles.

As she made coffee, Florin filled her mind. He was her dream man. Kind, funny, interesting. What was there not to like? OK, he had an unusual job but did that change him as a man?

When she joined him, Florin was warming his hands by the fire.

"Thanks, Nikki. I'll drink this and head back. We open the church to the homeless in poor weather so there'll be plenty for me to do when I get in."

"Are you ever off-duty?"

"Not often but I do get down time. It's not all saving souls and charitable deeds."

She laughed, handing him his jacket.

"Look, Nikki, I'll be honest. I like you. Really like you. And I want to see more of you. I know my job's scared you. I get it all the time. I don't mean I'm always chatting up gorgeous women, just that

Saint's. His wife's an atheist and they still make it work. However my last girlfriend was a committed Christian but we split up."

Long after he'd left, his words lingered.

Florin was on her mind almost constantly, even at work, and it was there that she decided what to do.

She was calculating the risks for insuring a chain of hotels when she suddenly stopped and thought. Gazing out of the window one word echoed. *Risk.*

Reaching for her phone, she dialled Florin's number.

"Hey, fancy that cappuccino at Drury's we never had?" she said.

"Do I? Yes, of course." He laughed.

OK, Florin had an unusual job… but did that change him as a man?

it changes people's perception of me. Not only women but builders, taxi drivers – shop assistants."

For a moment she considered how hard it must be for Florin.

"Of course, it's more than a job," he continued. "My faith's very important to me. But we're only just getting to know each other. My religion might prove a stumbling block in the future but then, so might anything. You could meet a vet who has strong political views you don't share. Or he might find you don't love animals as much as he does. Do you see?"

She understood. No matter who she met and how well she hoped it might turn out, she could discover something about that person – in fact, invariably she had – that brought the relationship to an end.

"My mate Ronnie's the vicar at All

"Later today? Or tomorrow?"

"No, today – I don't want to waste another minute."

"Me neither!"

She ended the call and looked at her monitor. His job was about faith, but hers was all about calculated risk. So wasn't it time she took a chance with her love life, too? OK, his religion might prove to be a problem but how would they know, if they never took the first step to find out?

Life was a gamble and Florin, she smiled, was a risk well worth taking…

Love reading great fiction? Don't miss My Weekly on sale on Tuesdays.

The Queen Of
Cosy Crime

It seems that bestselling writer Irene is facing a challenge from a young pretender…

By Glenda Young

I s this your first time?" Irene asked.

Ben nodded his head.

"You're very quiet," she said.

"I like being quiet," Ben replied. "It helps clear my head while I put my thoughts in order."

"I remember my first time, only too well," Irene said. "To be honest, there are times when I wish I didn't. There were only three people in the audience and one of them fell asleep halfway through."

Irene glanced at Ben as he rifled through his notes.

"You do know this is the first time I've been asked to speak about my books along with another writer?" she said. "I've never had to share a stage before. I'm usually the main, and if I may say so, the exclusive attraction."

"It's not exactly my idea of fun, either," said Ben, curtly. "It was our agent's idea for us to do this talk together."

Irene arched an eyebrow at Ben but he pretended not to notice.

"And our agent knows we're both very twee and cosy and I'm…"

"I know exactly what you are," Irene said with a hint of menace in her voice.

"You're the best of the new breed of crime writers, apparently. Let me think now, how did our agent describe you to me? Oh yes, I remember. You were lauded as *the contender for my cosy crime crown.*"

Ben shifted slightly, his body language giving away how uncomfortable Irene's words were.

"But I'm not ready to hand it over," she said. "I've got a few more novels in me, just you mark my words. And anyway, there's nothing wrong with writing about families. I wouldn't be where I am today if it wasn't for my own."

Thinking about her family, a wave of anxiety hit Irene. She couldn't help but worry about her eldest daughter who was working out of hours on a big project later that night.

Just then, Cathryn Harris, the crime-writing festival organiser, popped her head around the door.

"Five minutes to showtime!" she said through an over-bright smile. "Would you like to follow me to the stage? The hall's standing room only. They're all looking forward to meeting Irene McGovern, the queen of cosy crime!"

Ben gave a little cough.

"Oh, and you, Ben. They're all looking forward to meeting you, too."

Cathryn walked confidently to the front of the stage and the audience immediately hushed. She gave a short opening speech and asked the audience to welcome to the stage the country's two very best crime writers.

"Ladies and gentlemen," Cathryn said into her microphone. "Firstly, we are delighted to bring you a novelist whose name you may not have heard. But believe me, you will know his name soon. He's the new contender for the cosy **Continued overleaf** crime crown, the newest talent in town – please welcome Ben Horne!"

Ben walked onto the stage to a polite clapping from the audience. He walked to his allocated chair and looked out to the sea of faces. Cathryn tapped her microphone and carried on. "And now, ladies and gentlemen, it is my pleasure to present to you the queen of cosy crime herself, it's the bestselling crime writer Irene McGovern!"

When Irene walked to the stage the audience erupted into an explosion of clapping and cheering. She even got a standing ovation. Carefully and slowly, Irene eased herself into her chair.

Cathryn took the seat in the middle

audience. "Would you like me to hang up my cosy crime crown, folks?" she asked the crowd.

A roar of disapproval filled the hall.

"I think that's your answer," Irene said to Cathryn.

"Then let me tell you this, Irene," said Cathryn, beaming another smile. "Ben Horne's latest book has, so far this year, proved to be the fastest-selling crime novel of the decade."

The audience gave a polite round of applause at this news and Ben nodded towards the audience in thanks. But it was news that Irene didn't know.

Why hadn't her agent told her this young upstart's book had sold faster than hers? Irene began to wonder what else

Ben was in the zone, his mind clearing, inspiration replacing his earlier anxiety

between Irene and Ben. She interviewed both authors, starting with Ben and working up to the top billing author, Irene. She took questions from the audience and let both authors publicise their new books as best as they could.

So busy was Cathryn moderating the discussion between Irene and Ben that she missed the look of envy that Ben sent Irene's way. And she missed the look of derision that Irene sent back.

"Irene, you've been writing crime novels for over forty years," Cathryn said. "And you've had thirty books published. Do you think it might be time for you to hang up your cosy crime crown and pass it on to the younger generation of writers? Writers like Ben, here, perhaps?"

Irene smiled sweetly out into the

the agent was keeping from her.

Cathryn checked her watch.

"Ladies and gentlemen, we have time for just one more question."

A hand shot up in the front row.

"Yes, the lady in the red coat?" Cathryn smiled.

"My question is for Ben Horne. Ben, I'm interested to know whether you have a special place where you like to plot your stories?"

Ben cleared his throat.

"I like to run a lot," he said. "I find that running clears my head and allows me to think. And being a crime writer, I like to run in the dark and dead of night, to get inspiration for my work."

"Thank you," said the woman in the red coat, smiling.

After the festival ended, Irene was driven home in her blue Jaguar car. She kept the red one for weekends.

"James?" she asked her driver. "Did my agent call while I was at the festival?"

"No, Mrs McGovern," he replied. "Not that I'm aware of."

Irene drummed her fingers on the warm leather of the heated car seat.

Ben Horne drove home from the festival in his battered blue Mini that he couldn't afford to replace. Not yet, anyway. But his new book was already selling faster than Irene McGovern's and becoming the king of cosy crime couldn't be too far away.

Arriving home, he decided to go out for a run. He headed to the canal towpath, his favourite place to run and think. After a few minutes working up a sweat, his thoughts began to unfurl.

Ben was in the zone, his mind clearing, ideas and inspiration filling the space taken up earlier by anxiety over giving his first writer's talk.

Concentrating intensely on a plot for his new novel, Ben didn't notice the flash of red as an arm jerked out of the darkness, throwing him off balance.

The flash of red came at him again and again, this time connecting harder and faster, pounding his body, piercing his skin. Ben stumbled and reached out in the darkness to steady himself.

But in the confusion he fell, the ground under his feet turned to water, and his body sank, sucked down into the canal's deep and murky depths.

News of the death of Ben Horne didn't even trend on Twitter, Irene noticed the next day.

Irene's phone rang. It was her new agent inviting her to give a writer's talk.

"How are you fixed for next Friday in Southland Village Hall? We've got another young crime writer on our books. She's really up and coming, Susie Atkins, very talented girl. I thought I'd stick her on the stage with you, give her a bit of exposure, you know – it'll be her first writer's talk."

Irene checked her calendar.

"Looks fine to me," she said. "Book me in and email the details."

After the publisher hung up, Irene sent a text message. It simply read:

Southland Village Hall. Friday next. Susie Atkins.

At exactly the same time as Irene sent her text message, a signed copy of her new crime novel was delivered to a first floor apartment in town.

And at precisely the same moment as the novel arrived, a phone inside the apartment pinged with a text message.

It was an apartment that had a coat stand in the hallway. A coat stand with a red coat hanging from it.

Pausing beside the coat stand, a woman ripped open a Jiffy bag and opened the novel. She smiled when she saw the familiar handwriting inside the front cover.

For helping the queen keep her crown. Love and thanks, Mum x

• •

MY FAVOURITE...

Now, Voyager with Bette Davis and Paul Henreid is my top film, for "poor Aunt Charlotte's" transformation from browbeaten frump to glamorous femme fatale! *Audrey Patterson, Fashion Editor*

On The Same Page

As life takes another unexpected turn, it's a perfect time to look back on all our happy years together…

By Deborah Murphy

I peer over the newspaper and watch you as you read, admiring your strong hands with their long tapering fingers.

You wear glasses now and your raven-black hair is streaked with silver, but it suits you. You catch me looking and smile over at me.

Henry Galbraith, the boy with the soulful brown eyes who could see straight into my heart. He's still there, the boy I met and married 20 years ago.

You go back to your book and I click my pen closed and then open it again, pretending to puzzle over a really tough clue in the crossword, but really I'm remembering the day we met.

It was a warm day in early September and I was sitting on the daisy-speckled grass at the side of a slow-moving river with my best friend, Emma. We were watching as the university rowing team practised, waving as the boys rowed by, all bravado and bluster. Emma was interested in the coxswain and we were plotting her plan of seduction when I looked across the park and saw you.

You were walking in the middle of a large group, the centre of attention. Whatever you had just said made everyone laugh and you laughed along with them. One of your group knew Emma and he shouted over a hello. You glanced over to see who he was greeting, the smile still on your lips.

You nodded to Emma first, then you turned your attention to me. And the world stood still. Our eyes locked and in that second no-one else existed.

We weren't properly introduced until November when we met in a pub on quiz night. Your lot from the Maths department were pitted against us in the final; despite being called Universally Challenged, they gave us a real run for our money.

But we were victorious and you were very gracious in defeat, shaking hands with us all in turn, your warm smile and good looks winning over the all-girl team. I knew you were as keen on me as I was on you when you held onto my hand and gaze, so it wasn't a surprise when you asked if I fancied going for a curry. And so our story began.

The twins were born a year after our

Continued overleaf

Continued from previous page
graduation. By then you were working for a high street bank and I had a job in a school library.

When I look back on the childhood we gave our girls, I remember all the happy times – the summer holidays where the rain drummed a steady beat on the caravan roof, decorating the Christmas tree with spiced gingerbread men, Easter egg hunts, birthday parties… the list goes on.

Now the twins are first year University students themselves. I couldn't be more proud of them and I know you feel the same.

Not that there weren't hard times too. When you lost your job at the bank, my heart went out to you. And even though you found something else fairly quickly, the taint of redundancy stayed with you for a while.

And then when the girls were twelve, at such a crucial stage in their lives, I became very ill. Even today I find it too difficult to think about. It's enough to say that after months of gruelling treatment I pulled through, and we became stronger as a couple and as a family. We stopped taking the good things in life for granted.

"Do you fancy a cuppa, May, love?" you ask, bringing me back to reality. You walk over to me and kiss the top of my head and I smile up at you from the hospital bed.

Suddenly I know that everything is going to be just fine. After all these years, through the highs and the lows, the twists and turns, we're still on the same page.

"I'd love one!" I reply, counting every one of my blessings. "Actually," I say. "Do you know what I'd really like? Chicken curry. So grab your coat, mister," I say with a wink. "I think it's time we helped this little one along!"

I rub my baby bump contentedly as you leave to buy me the meal we ate on our first night together. And so our story continues with baby number three imminent. I've never loved you more.

● ●

MY FAVOURITE…

My favourite film is *Frozen* – it's so much fun and I admit I can't help bursting into song with all the great musical numbers!
Gillian Petrie, picture researcher

Festive Savoury Frittatas

Ingredients (Serves 12)

- ◆ **20g butter**
- ◆ **1 small red pepper, deseeded and finely chopped**
- ◆ **1 bunch spring onions, very finely chopped**
- ◆ **2 large eggs**
- ◆ **300ml milk**
- ◆ **1tsp mixed dried herbs**
- ◆ **100g Cheddar cheese, finely grated**
- ◆ **Salt and freshly ground black pepper**
- ◆ **Rocket or fresh herb sprigs, to garnish**

1 Preheat the oven to 180°C, Fan oven 160°C, Gas Mark 4.

2 Melt butter in a frying pan. Gently fry pepper and spring onions for 3-4min, until soft. Remove from the heat.

3 Beat together the eggs and milk. Stir in the herbs, grated cheese and cooked vegetables. Season. Spoon into a greased, non-stick mini-muffin tin or bun tin (a flexible one works well). Bake for 20-25min, until set and golden. Allow to cool, then remove.

4 Serve, garnished with rocket or sprigs of fresh herbs.

RECIPE AND FOOD STYLING: SUE ASHWORTH PHOTOGRAPHY JONATHAN SHORT

Christmas Cheer

When your heart is full of love to give, does it matter who you end up sharing it with?

by Pippa Newnton

Outside the snow cascaded down. The trees bowed under the sparkling white covering. There was a sense that the earth was waiting. Inside the house, two people were huddled over a small fire.

Sue was sitting thoughtfully reading the newspaper.

"I see there's more of those refugees coming over. Poor things, leaving everything behind and having only the clothes they stand up in."

"Why do they come?" Andy asked.

"What alternative do they have? Their country's being destroyed, their families split up."

"It makes you realise how lucky we are," Andy said pragmatically.

"I know," Sue sighed. "But it's Christmas Eve tomorrow and this year it's going to be all different. I don't know why Vicky couldn't come to us for Christmas."

"Come on, Sue, she's married and got a baby of her own – of course they want to do their own thing. We've sent them their presents."

"The place just feels empty." Sue looked round the room. Familiar things looked back at her; the cushion Vicky had embroidered for her birthday, the poinsettia Vicky had sent them for Christmas.

The Christmas tree sat forlornly in the corner waiting to be decorated. She couldn't find the energy to start on it.

"We're getting old," she said mournfully, almost to herself.

"As old as you feel." Andy got up and crossed to the box of decorations. "Come on, let's get the job done. I'll put a carols CD on, that should cheer you up."

"No, it won't. I'll feel worse." Sue snuggled down into the nest of cushions she had made on the sofa.

Andy looked at his wife and put his arm gently round her shoulders.

"Where's that get-up-and-go spirit?"

Sue smiled wanly. She realised that she must make an effort. So she got up and helped Andy with the tree, and then they strung up the sparkly garlands round the walls, hanging tinsel over the pictures. Finally she assembled the crib and set the tiny figures of Joseph and Mary, the shepherds, the three Wise Men and the animals in their places.

"I must admit," she said, "it does cheer

the place up a bit – but Christmas is for families, and we don't feel like a family any more now Vicky's gone."

Making a renewed effort, she said, "You'd better drive me down to the supermarket, I'll get some goodies in. I haven't felt like it before, but you're right, love – just because we're on our own, it's no call not to celebrate."

"That's the spirit – get your coat on, then, and let's go."

Once in the car, Sue began to feel better. Andy drove past their neighbours' houses decorated with lights outlining Christmas bells, holly, and a Father Christmas with his reindeer.

"We ought to do something like that," she said pensively.

"Too late this year, but perhaps next," Andy said, glancing at the decorations.

They drove to the supermarket. It was full of happy, laughing people standing in the aisles – families with children, older people standing talking.

Andy pushed the trolley while Sue loaded it up with Christmas fare.

"Mustn't forget the Christmas pudding," she said, sighing. "I remember the days when my mum used to make the pudding and we had to find the silver **Continued overleaf**

Continued from previous page

sixpence she'd hidden in the mixture."

"How about a bottle of champagne?" Andy said, heading for the wine section. "Let's push the boat out."

That made Sue feel sad. *I suppose we must make the best of it,* she thought.

Between them they loaded their purchases into the boot of the car and set off back to the house.

Suddenly Andy stopped the car abruptly. There in the middle of the road was a young girl, clutching a small bundle.

"What's she trying to do? Kill herself?" Andy looked stunned.

Sue wound the window down and called out, "What's the matter, love?"

"Come on, Andy, let's take her home."

"You can't do that," he said. "She must belong somewhere."

"We'll sort that out when we get home," she said firmly.

Andy, shrugged and drove on.

At the house Sue helped the girl indoors, still clutching her baby.

She had scarcely settled her on the sofa when there was the sound of a motorbike and a loud knock at the door.

"Answer that, Andy," she said.

Andy went to the door and opened it. To his surprise a large, bearded man stood there. Andy staggered back.

"Excuse, but my wife is here?" the

"She's only a child," he said quietly. "And that's a baby she's got there"

The girl woke as though from a trance and moved over to the window.

It was a cold day. The snow was still falling but the girl had on only a light coat.

"You'll freeze," Sue said in concern. "Come into the car and get warm."

Andy got out and opened the rear door, helping her in.

"She's only a child," he said quietly as he slid back into the driving seat. "And that's a baby she's got there."

Sue turned round to see that the girl was crying.

"What's your name?" she asked.

The girl looked up, wiping her eyes.

"I am Mary. You are very kind to me and my baby."

"Where were you going?" asked Sue.

"I have nowhere," the girl said.

Sue made up her mind on the spot.

man asked in gentle tones.

Before he could say anything, the girl got up and rushed to the door.

"Yusef, you come for me!"

Andy stood aside to let the man in. Yusef embraced his wife.

"I have found shelter," he said.

"These kind people have taken me in. I was worried you had gone," Mary said.

"All right now. You come." He cradled the baby in his arms. "Everything will be all right now."

"Wait!" Sue thought quickly. She packed some of their Christmas goodies into a bag, along with the half pack of nappies Vicky had left behind on her last visit. "Here – take these." She handed the bag to Mary.

"Thank you – thank you, kind people," Mary said, tears in her eyes once more.

Carefully Yusef put Mary, still clutching the child, on the pillion of the bike, mounted it and with a wave was off.

"Now what shall we do?" Andy said. "You've given away half of our Christmas treats to two strangers."

He looked so disappointed at the loss of his sausage rolls that Sue wanted to hug him.

"I've a feeling about those two. In any case it's good to give – especially when it looked as if they have nothing. At least they can have a little Christmas cheer now."

"You're right, of course and we've got each other – let's make the best of it." Andy put his arm round her shoulder.

Before he could say anything else the phone rang. Sue answered it.

"It's Vicky," she said in surprise. "Hello, love, is everything all right?"

"We want you to come and spend Christmas with us," Vicky said. "Luke and I talked it over and realised that you would be lonely. Luke doesn't have any folks as you know, and we realised it wouldn't be Christmas without our family around us."

"We'll come – won't we, Andy?" Sue's face lit up.

"Sorry it's such short notice, but just jump in the car and come," Vicky said.

"It's not quite as easy as that," her mother said, "but yes, we'll be there as soon as we can."

Sue rushed around, prodding Andy into action. They loaded the car and set off.

Vicky and Luke lived in a new-build detached house. As Andy drove up to the front of the house, Vicky rushed out to welcome them. Luke came out, shook hands and ushered them in. Vicky embraced her mother.

Later, everything unloaded, Sue looked around the small, neat house. She was pleased that her daughter had made a good marriage, had a good man, and a baby boy whom she loved at first sight.

"I've brought you this," she said, holding out a cardboard box.

"But you've given us presents already," Vicky protested.

"This is special," Sue said. "It's something you've had since you were a child."

Vicky sat down, opening the box quickly. She exclaimed, "My crib. Oh, thank you – but I thought you wanted to keep it?"

"No – it's yours now and you can hand it down so it stays in the family."

Later that evening, drinks in hand, they were relaxing in front of a real coal fire when Sue got up and crossed to the crib set out on a table under the window.

Looking out, she saw one star shining brighter than the others. Gazing up, she said quietly, "Christmas is for families. I hope Yusef and Mary are as lucky as we are." Raising her glass she turned and toasted her family.

MY FAVOURITE...

The Nativity is my favourite story. It means many things to different people, but its underlying theme is that family is so important – that and a little kindness can go a long way.

Nutcracker Magic

The drama is all backstage as Claire creates perfection and then havoc – but who can help her out of trouble?

By Jan Snook

Claire cut off the final thread and stuck the needle into the pin-cushion. That was it. The final costume! She stood up and carefully hung the glittering garment on the rail marked *Sugar Plum Fairy*, then swathed it in a cotton cover. All done.

She had been working on the costumes for *The Nutcracker* ever since she joined the company six months ago. Straight out of art college, where she had specialised in costume design, she had been thrilled to land the job in the costume department of a ballet company – even if some of her friends did think it was a bit menial.

"You'll just be sewing," James had said, disappointed. "You're a designer, not a dressmaker, don't sell yourself short!"

Claire's heart had sunk. James, the supercool, supertalented star of their year thought she'd done the wrong thing. The one person she would have liked to impress. The person she'd been dreaming about since her first day at art school.

She'd taken the job anyway. It was a start, and a pretty good one, she reckoned. And what was James doing? He was still trawling his portfolio around the top fashion houses without any luck.

"Take anything they offer you," she'd said to him. "Get a foot in the door. You don't know what it could lead to."

But he was adamant; he was an artist.

Claire looked around. She had done the right thing, for her, at least. Here she was, in a workroom filled with tulle and velvets and satins and pearls and sequins, all in jewel-like colours. She was perfectly content.

On another table Maureen was putting the finishing touches to a magnificent tiara.

"Claire," Maureen called, "could you do me a favour? Could you come and try this on? I just need to see where to put this final bead."

Claire agreed happily. What girl wouldn't want to try on a glittering headdress?

"That's it for me tonight," Maureen said once the bead was in place. "So we're all set for tomorrow, then? This is a bit of a record, having all the costumes ready the day before the Opening Night – even if it is almost midnight… See you in the morning. You are coming to the performance tomorrow, aren't you?"

"Well, I was hoping to watch it from the wings…" Claire tailed off.

"What? You haven't got a ticket? Oh, what a shame – perhaps the box office ran out of freebies. You'll probably be able to watch one later on." The woman looked at her watch and quickly jammed the tiara onto a waiting polystyrene head. "I'm late. Don't stay too long – there's rain forecast. You'll lock up, will you?"

Claire nodded and watched her friend – well, her immediate boss, in fact – depart. This was what she liked. Being alone with all the sumptuous fabrics, the gold leaf, the silver threads, the crystal beads and the shimmering ribbons.

She could dream she was the one going on stage, pretend she was the Sugar Plum Fairy, ethereal and light as a feather. Not that she'd ever been graceful enough! Still. A girl could dream, couldn't she?

In fact, Claire thought, suddenly daring

Continued overleaf

and conscious of being the only person in the building, perhaps a girl could do more than dream. She went to the completed costume and removed its cotton wrapper, letting the jewel-encrusted satin top slip between her fingers. Surely it would fit?

With trembling hands she undid the fastenings on the lustrous tutu. It was a fairytale costume, and she gazed at it with pride. Then, looking around nervously, Claire took off her jeans and top, and slipped the tutu on. It would be a useful exercise, she justified it to herself. She'd be able to see if there were any problems she hadn't considered as she was making it. She pulled the satin top up carefully, and stood in front of the mirror. All she

simple seam. The tiara, too, was damaged, and she didn't even know how to repair that. Claire pulled the costume gently off and put her own clothes back on before she dared examine the tutu.

It was ruined. Two panels of the bodice had torn right across, and beads were tinkling as they fell on the bare floorboards.

Even if she could repair it – and that was a big "if" – it would take hours and hours of work. All night. Probably well into tomorrow morning, and she was practically asleep as it was.

She could feel panic enveloping her. Who could she possibly call at this late hour? With trembling fingers she picked up her phone.

"What we need is coffee," he said firmly. "It's going to be a very long night"

needed was the tiara. She crossed the room on tiptoe, aware that she was being silly – there was no-one to hear her. Then she placed the headdress on her own dark curls. A quick twirl…

The deafening clap of unseasonal thunder made Claire jump. She slipped and fell, hearing the more terrifying sound of fabric ripping as she hit the floor.

She closed her eyes. This could not be happening. She had no time to mend a seam. How could she have been so stupid? She got to her feet slowly, aware that she had twisted her ankle, and felt behind her, trying to establish how much damage she'd done. Her fingers met ribbons of frayed fabric. It didn't feel like a

James arrived twenty minutes later. She met him at the stage door and led him through the dimly-lit labyrinthine corridors, past the towering Christmas tree from the first act, past still-drying scenery shimmering with silvery crystals, past the cylinders of dry ice that made the snow scenes so magical, until at last they arrived back at the workroom.

Claire was white and trembling, her ankle swelling, and on the verge of more tears. James took charge.

"What we need is coffee," he said firmly. "It's going to be a long night."

He set to, unpicking the seam that joined the skirt to the bodice, while Claire found the fabrics, sequins and beads she needed to replace the torn panels for the top. Together they cut, basted, stitched, pressed, lined, sequinned, beaded and reassembled, working in near silence with occasional exclamations of frustration or cries of horror as they looked at the clock.

"It's almost four in the morning," Claire moaned as James brought her yet another cup of strong coffee. "Only another few hours and people will start arriving for work, and there's still such a lot to do…"

"It'll be fine," James said, putting the finishing touches to the tiara, which he had tackled remarkably skilfully. "Stop worrying. Is there a finer beading needle somewhere? This one won't go through these crystals…"

At six they heard the first sounds of the building coming to life as cleaners let themselves in. James was attaching the tulle skirt to the bodice as Claire put away the tell-tale array of fabrics and threads that had accumulated on the work table.

"You'd better go," she whispered as he finished. "I'll be able to finish off now, I think. And obviously I'll never be able to thank you enough, James. You've probably saved my job. I'll talk to you later, OK?"

James kissed her on the cheek, and Claire was threading another needle before he was even out of the room. She could hardly keep her eyes open as she attached the last few beads, and swayed when she finally stood up to put the tutu back under its cotton wrap on the rail.

"Claire! Claire!"

Had her alarm not gone off? Was she going to be late for work?

"Claire!" the voice shouted again, closer to her ear this time. Slowly Claire opened her eyes. Maureen was patting her hand and gazing at her in concern.

"Claire? Have you been here all night?"

Claire looked around at the grey light in the work room, and her glance slid quickly to the rail. The costume was still there, hopefully in one piece. It was all right. No-one need ever know. She tried to smile, but her lower lip wobbled dangerously, and before she knew what was happening she was sobbing.

"The Sugar Plum Fairy costume," she gulped. "I ruined it! I've been sewing all night…"

But the rest of the sentence was lost in more sobs.

Maureen was looking at her, uncomprehending. Then she went and fetched the costume and started examining it.

"Claire," another voice said, and Claire and Maureen turned to see the costume department director standing in the doorway. He'd obviously been there for a couple of minutes, because he suddenly smiled.

"You must have fallen asleep on the job, Claire. You've been dreaming, that's all. Just like Clara in the ballet!

"Nothing's happened to the costume, has it, Maureen? Poor Claire! Here all night and then waking up in a panic! All because of a silly nightmare. You'd better get off home again and rest – everything's done, isn't it, Maureen?"

Maureen was smiling and nodding as the director swept out. Then she picked up the tiara. Claire got to her feet and quickly sat down again with a yelp of **Continued overleaf**

Continued from previous page
pain. Her ankle was swollen quite impressively and throbbing.

"But you've hurt yourself," Maureen said, concerned. "I suppose that happened when you fell? Were you trying the costume on?" There was a long silence.

"What I can't understand," Maureen said, "is how you got all this done overnight. Unless there was some magical *Nutcracker* prince who came to help you?"

"How did you know?" Claire whispered.

"Let's see… two coffee mugs? That and the fact that the tiara now has these rather pretty pewter beads instead of gold. Who put them on, by the way? It's very skilfully done…" Claire looked up to see Maureen smiling.

"Don't worry. No-one else will know the difference, and we've all had accidents at some time or another. No, what we need now is to find you a couple of tickets for tonight's performance. You can't stand in the wings on that ankle. And anyway, I'd like to meet your *Nutcracker* prince. We could do with someone like him. Does he by any chance need a job?"

"Well yes, but… his name's James…"

Was she still dreaming? A shadowy figure was standing in the doorway.

"Oh," Claire said weakly, "he's here."

"I just called at your flat thinking you might need a lift into work, what with your ankle and everything," James said, crossing the room and looking at Claire with concern, "and they said you never got home! I've been worried sick."

Claire caught Maureen's amused look as he bent down and kissed her. Two kisses in one night! And he'd called to give her a lift? All was evidently not lost!

"And is there really a job going…?" he asked hopefully.

The next twelve hours passed in a whirl. James talked to the director about the job, then took Claire back to her flat and let her sleep, her foot propped up, while he napped on the sofa.

After making her an early supper, he brought her back to the theatre, armed with the two promised tickets, and they sat in the auditorium, listening to the growing excitement as the audience arrived: little girls in velvet party dresses with eyes shining, elegant women and men in black tie, the great and good from the ballet world.

The lights dimmed, the curtain went up, and James took Claire's hand…

Which just went to prove, Claire reflected as James went to get them a drink during the interval, that sometimes fairy tales did come true. She was still smiling at this when Maureen approached.

"I've had so many compliments on the costumes," she said, looking around. "I'm so glad Cinderella managed to get to the ball – or the ballet. But where's Prince Charming?"

But hang on – that's a different fairy tale altogether!

● ●

MY FAVOURITE…

Ballet and needlework are two of my favourite things, so combining the two would be my dream job. It only took the question "But what if…?" to turn a daydream into this story!

My Weekly

Favourite Celebrities

Up-to-date Health News

Fabulous Fiction

PLUS

Puzzles

Cookery

Fashion

Beauty

Real Life

You'll Love It!
On Sale Every Tuesday